OPERATIONAL AMPLIFIERS:
Theory and Servicing

OPERATIONAL AMPLIFIERS:
Theory and Servicing

by Edward Bannon

RESTON PUBLISHING COMPANY, INC.
A Prentice-Hall Company
Reston, Virginia   22090

Library of Congress Cataloging in Publication Data

Bannon, Edward
   Operational amplifiers.
   x, 195 p. illus.
   Includes index.
   1.   Operational amplifiers.   I.   Title.
TK7871.58.06H47   621.3815'35   74-34298
ISBN   0-87909-585-7

TECHNICAL DRAWINGS BY ROBERT MOSHER

10 9 8 7 6 5 4 3 2 1

PRINTED IN THE UNITED STATES OF AMERICA

TABLE OF CONTENTS

PREFACE

With the rapid advance of the operational-amplifier field in recent years, a need has arisen for a relevant state-of-the-art textbook. Monolithic operational amplifiers have become more sophisticated and versatile, and the voltage op amp is now supplemented by the transconductance op amp. This device has made a complete transition from an analog-computer subassembly to a universal analog component. It may now be regarded as an elaborated and sophisticated offspring from the conventional transistor. The first-generation IC op amps provided high input impedance, low output impedance, and high voltage gain. They were, however, susceptible to latch-up, short-circuit damage, and required external lag networks.

Second-generation op amps were immune to latch-up, included output short-circuit protection, and contained built-in lag networks. They also provided higher input impedance, higher voltage gain, and lower input offset and bias currents. Third-generation op amps provided still lower input offset and bias currents, with greater immunity to temperature drift. Fourth-generation op amps offered further improvement of an order or more of magnitude in reduction of input offset and bias currents and immunity to temperature drift. Fifth-generation op amps featured greatly increased frequency range and faster slew rate, with other functional improvements. It is probable that the operational transconductance amplifier, with its high output impedance, should be classified as a sixth-generation device. The operational transconductance amplifier facilitates the implementation of sophisticated networks, such as gyrators.

It is the purpose of this textbook to present a broad coverage of basic op-amp applications, with appropriate theoretical treatment for use as a teaching tool in the junior college curriculum. Troubleshooting is explained along with basic theory. The focus of attention is on the beginning student and his problems. Mathematical treatment has been introduced only to the extent required for ample rigor at this instructional level. It is assumed that the student has completed courses in electricity, electronics, and radio communication, or has attained a practical background in these areas. A student who is taking a concurrent course in semiconductor electronics will be able to assimilate the associated chapters in this text by looking up various terms and topics with which he may be unfamiliar. The burden on the student will be considerably lightened, however, if he has completed courses in both general electronics and semiconductor electronics before starting his study of operational amplifiers.

Acknowledgment is made to those who have preceded the author by their development of other books on op-amp technology, and to the faculty of San Jose City College, who have made many helpful suggestions and criticisms. This book can properly be described as a team effort, although the individual members would choose to minimize the measure of their own contributions. It is appropriate that this textbook be dedicated as a teaching tool to the instructors and students of our junior colleges and technical schools.

EDWARD BANNON

1 · Basic Operational Amplifiers

1.1 GENERAL CONSIDERATIONS

Operational amplifiers (op amps) received their name from designers of first-generation analog computers. An operational amplifier was a somewhat specialized amplifier section or block in these early computer systems. Computers can be classified into two basic categories: analog and digital. An analog computer operates on directly measurable quantities, such as voltages, which represent numbers. Analog voltages are continuously variable. A digital computer also operates with directly measurable quantities, such as voltages, which represent numbers. However, digital voltages are constant in value and are merely switched on or off—digital voltages are not variable. Op amps are used primarily in analog computers. In addition to the analog and digital types of computers, a subclassification is termed the hybrid type of computer. A hybrid computer employs both continuously variable analog voltages and switched digital voltages. Operational amplifiers are used in hybrid computers. Op amps are also utilized in other kinds of electronic equipment.

During the course of op-amp development, tubes, transistors, and integrated circuits have been employed. Both hybrid and monolithic integrated circuits have found application. A hybrid integrated circuit is an arrangement that consists of one or more IC's combined with one or more discrete component parts. A hybrid IC may also consist of a combination of more than one type of integrated circuit joined into one integrated component. Again, a monolithic IC consists of elements which are formed upon or within a semiconductor substrate with at least one of the elements formed within the substrate. In other words, an integrated circuit is a combination of interconnected circuit elements inseparably associated on or within a continuous substrate.

Today, the monolithic integrated circuit has become the most widely used type of op amp. A typical op amp is illustrated in Figure 1–1. Op-amp IC's have become comparatively economical and are applied as building blocks in electronic computers, waveform processors, active filters, and so on as detailed in following chapters. An op amp is basically a dc-coupled multistage linear amplifier. Note that a linear amplifier has an output waveform amplitude that is directly proportional to its input signal amplitude. An ideal op amp would have in-

Fig. 1–1 Appearance of a typical operational amplifier.

finite input impedance and infinite gain. In practice, an op amp has extremely high input impedance; its current driving requirement is measured in pA ($\mu\mu$A). A preferred-type op amp has a voltage gain of approximately 100,000 times. An output impedance of 150 ohms is typical.

Figure 1–2 shows the internal circuit of a widely used op amp. Note that two inputs are provided. One is called the inverting input, and the other is called the noninverting input. Together, they form a differential input arrangement. One input is said to be the complement, or the inverse, of the other. In other words, if a small positive voltage is applied to the noninverting (+) input terminal, it will produce a positive output. On the other hand, if the same small positive voltage is applied to the inverting (−) input terminal, it will produce a negative output. Note that if the same voltage were applied to both input terminals at the same time, the output would be zero. If desired, both input terminals can be driven; this is called the differential connection. Or, one input terminal can be driven and the other input terminal returned to ground; this is called the single-ended connection.

An ideal op amp would have zero output when both input terminals are at zero potential. However, in practice, the output may not be exactly zero when both input terminals are at zero potential. This deviation from zero is called offset; some op amps provide connections to an external control which can compensate for offset voltage by applying suitable bias current to the input transistors. Observe the offset terminals provided in the configuration of Figure 1–2. Details of external circuitry are explained in following chapters. Note that an op amp has single-ended output. The output section operates in the emitter-follower mode to provide substantial power at low impedance.

1.2 BASIC APPLICATIONS

In most op-amp applications, only part of the full device gain is utilized. In other words, negative feedback is provided, as shown in Figure 1–3(a) and (b). These are examples of basic inverting and noninverting amplifiers. Note that the inclusion of the resistive divider network R_o–R_i provides negative feedback by channeling part of the output voltage to the inverting input terminal. In turn, the gain of the amplifier is equal to the sum of R_o and R_i divided by the value of R_i. Observe that the inverting input terminal is driven in Figure 1–3(a), whereas the noninverting input terminal is driven in (b). Next, the voltage summer shown in Figure 1–3(c) represents a slight elaboration of the inverting amplifier arrangement. It provides an output voltage

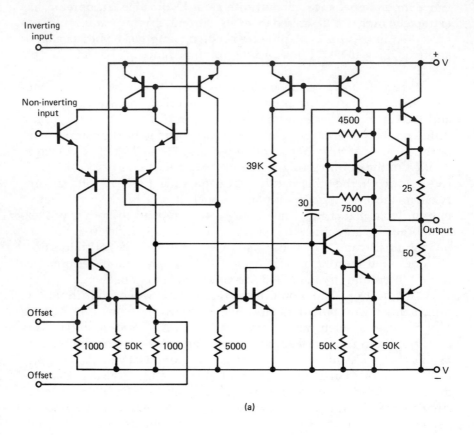

(a)

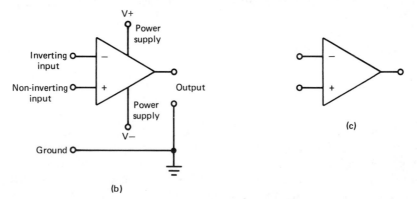

(b)

(c)

Fig. 1–2 Typical internal circuitry and symbols for op amps: **(a)** Internal configuration; **(b)** Elaborated symbol; **(c)** Simplified symbol.

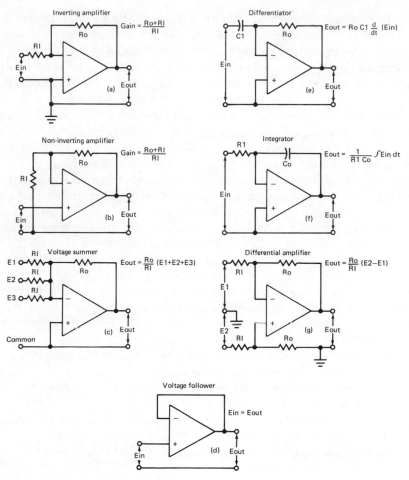

Fig. 1–3 Basic op-amp applications.

which is the sum of all the input voltages multiplied by the gain of the op amp. A voltage summer is often used as an audio mixer.

Next, Figure 1–3(d) depicts the basic voltage-follower arrangement. The output voltage follows the level of the input voltage precisely. Note that the load at the output of a voltage follower can draw a large current, although the input draws almost no current. A voltage follower is a special case of a noninverting amplifier in which the gain is unity. It is essentially an impedance transformer. An op-amp differentiator is shown in Figure 1–3(e). Although its action is analogous to that of a simple RC differentiating circuit, there is an important distinction in that an op-amp differentiator produces an output signal which is a precise derivative of the input waveform. In other words, the output signal approaches the true mathematical derivative of the input waveform. As an illustration, when an op-amp differentiator is driven by a square-wave voltage, the output consists of extremely narrow pulses. It will be shown later that extremely narrow pulses are developed because the differentiating capacitor "sees" an extremely low input impedance to the op amp.

An op-amp integrator is depicted in Figure 1–3(f). Although its action is analogous to that of a simple RC integrating circuit, there is an important distinction in that an op-amp integrator produces an output signal which is a precise integral of the input waveform. In other words, the output signal approaches the true mathematical integral of the input waveform. For example, when an op-amp integrator is driven by sharp pulses, the output consists of a precise square waveform. Note that op-amp integrators and differentiators perform opposite mathematical operations. As an illustration, if a square-wave voltage is applied to an op-amp differentiator, and the pulse output from the differentiator is applied to an op-amp integrator, a precise replica of the original square-wave voltage appears at the output of the integrator. If you are not fully familiar with the differentiating and integrating symbols indicated in Figure 1–3 (e) and (f), the following principles will be helpful:

1. A mathematically exact square wave has zero rise time and zero fall time; it has perfectly square corners and a perfectly flat top.
2. A mathematically exact impulse waveform has zero width and infinite amplitude.
3. The true mathematical derivative of a square wave is a sequence of alternately positive and negative impulse waveforms.
4. The true mathematical integral of an impulse waveform is a mathematically exact square wave.

Next, observe the op-amp differential-amplifier arrangement shown in Figure 1–3(g). This configuration is driven in push-pull and provides a single-ended output. Since negative feedback is provided, only part of the maximum available gain is realized. An important advantage of differential-amplifier operation is that common-mode signal voltages are cancelled out. As an illustration, when an audio signal flows through a long line, it may become mixed with hum interference. Note that if the line picks up stray hum fields, both sides of the line will develop hum voltage in the same phase. On the other hand, if the line is being driven by a push-pull audio signal, opposite sides of the line carry opposite-phase audio driving voltages. In other words, the hum voltage occurs as a single-ended driving voltage, whereas the audio signal is provided as a double-ended driving voltage. In this situation, the hum voltage is said to occur as common-mode interference. It follows from previous discussion that common-mode interference voltages will be cancelled out by a differential amplifier.

1.3 BASIC STABILITY CONSIDERATIONS

Op amps are high-gain devices, ranging up to a voltage gain of 1,000,000 times. Many op amps also have a frequency response from dc to several MHz. In turn, avoidance of spurious oscillation and considerations of general stability are of basic concern. Op-amp layouts should be arranged with the inputs well isolated from the output, and input leads should be kept as short as practical. To minimize the internal impedance (common coupling) that could be troublesome in the power source, the supply-voltage terminals are often bypassed with a $0.1-\mu F$ capacitor. Another stability consideration of importance is the inherent phase shift of the internal op-amp circuitry. In other words, as the operating frequency is increased, successive stages in an op amp introduce progressive phase shift from input to output. If this phase shift approaches 180 degrees before the gain has decreased to unity or less, the op amp will be unstable and break into oscillation. Therefore, an external phase-shift compensating network may be required, as exemplified by R1–C1 in Figure 1–4(a). This RC coupling introduces a progressive decrease in gain as the operating frequency increases. Some op amps have built-in phase-shift compensating networks, and require no external stabilizing components to avoid self-oscillation.

1.4 OPERATING CONDITIONS AND COMPONENT VALUES

Basic op-amp circuitry for various applications is shown in Figure 1–4. The majority of monolithic op-amp IC's operate from supply voltages of +5 to +15 volts, and −5 to −15 volts. It is sometimes practical to eliminate one supply-voltage polarity by using a resistive voltage divider to bias the noninverting input, as shown in Figure 1–4(c). An example of a limiting amplifier (clipper) is depicted in (d). A limiter is basically an overdriven amplifier; however, an ordinary Class-A amplifier does not necessarily operate satisfactorily as a limiter when it is overdriven. For example, to ensure that both positive and negative signal peaks are equally clipped, a potentiometer offset adjustment is required. Next, observe the comparator arrangement shown in Figure 1–4(e). A comparator has a unique function; it indicates when an input voltage becomes equal to a reference voltage. The output of a comparator

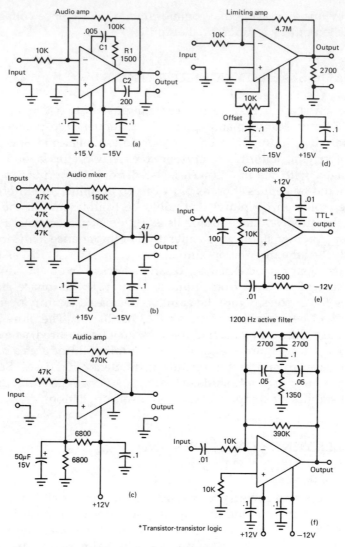

Fig. 1–4 Op-amp circuitry in typical applications.

swings from a maximum positive value to a maximum negative value as the input voltage passes through the reference voltage value. Comparators are used in frequency counters, for example, as explained in greater detail subsequently.

Op amps are used extensively in active filters, as exemplified in Figure 1–4(f). Note that a passive filter utilizes resistors and capacitors, for example. On the other hand, an active filter employs RC components in combination with an op amp. Low-pass, high-pass, bandpass, or band-reject (notch) filter action may be provided, as shown in Figure 1–5. In the example of Figure 1–4(f), a twin-T RC network is used in the negative-feedback loop. This twin-T network is resonant at 1200 Hz (has practically zero output at 1200 Hz). In turn, the op amp develops maximum gain at 1200 Hz with progressively reduced gain at higher frequencies and at lower frequencies. This frequency characteristic provides bandpass action. In this example, a gain of approximately 40 times is obtained at 1200 Hz. In addition to stepping up the amplitude of the input signal, amplifier action can provide a highly selective frequency response. This topic is treated in more detail in the following section.

1.5 BASIC LOW-PASS AND HIGH-PASS FILTERS

As we know, differentiators and integrators such as depicted in Figure 1–3(e) and (f) are forms of high-pass and low-pass filters. It is evident that they are also in the class of active filters. As would be anticipated, some active-filter arrangements are more elaborate than others, and the more complex configurations can provide various advantages in application and operation. It is instructive to consider the action of the single-loop feedback, low-pass active filter shown in Figure 1–6. This is called a single-loop feedback arrangement because there is only one feedback loop provided. Negative feedback takes place through the feedback component in (a), and through C_f and 10R in (b). We will find that filter action occurs both in the feedback component and in the input component, in this example.

Observe that filter action starts at the input circuit in Figure 1–6(b), where the incoming signal flows through a passive RC low-pass filter section and then into the op amp. Note that if C_f were disconnected, the op amp would merely step up the amplitude of the filter output. However, with C_f present in the feedback loop, additional low-pass filter action takes place. In other words, C_f has decreasing reactance at higher frequencies, with the result that more negative feedback occurs at higher frequencies. Therefore, the op amp develops higher gain at lower frequencies. The result of these combined low-pass filter actions is to produce a sharper cutoff characteristic than is provided by the passive RC filter alone.

It is helpful to note the meaning of certain op-amp terms at this point. With reference to Figure 1–6(a), V_s is called the input signal; V_i is called the differential input to the op amp; V_o is called the output of the op amp. The open-loop gain is defined as the ratio of V_o to V_i, or

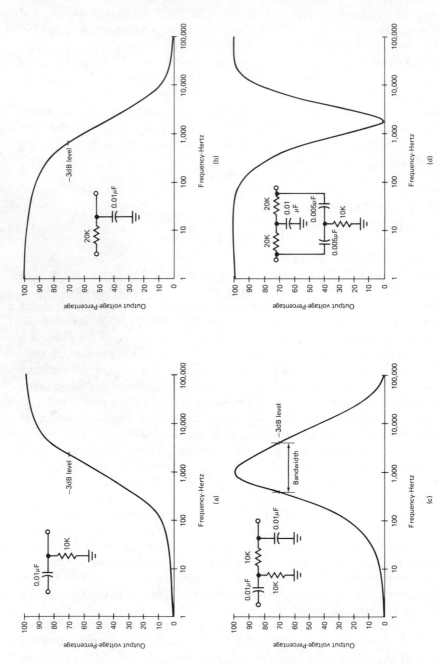

Fig. 1-5 Frequency characteristics of basic filters **(a)** High-pass frequency response; **(b)** Low-pass frequency response; **(c)** Band-pass frequency response; **(d)** Twin-T RC notch filter frequency response.

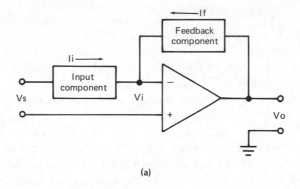

(a)

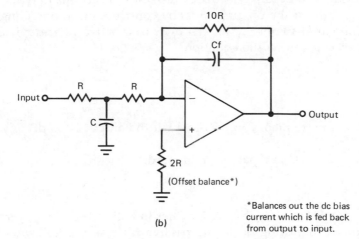

*Balances out the dc bias
current which is fed back
from output to input.

(b)

Fig. 1–6 A basic single-loop feedback low-pass active filter. **(a)** Block diagram;
(b) Basic circuit arrangement.

V_o/V_i. The closed-loop gain is defined as the ratio of V_o to V_s, or V_o/V_s.
Note carefully that the open-loop gain is the gain of the op amp, and is
independent of the input and feedback components. On the other hand,
the closed-loop gain depends only on the values of the input and feedback components, provided that the closed-loop gain of the circuit is
much less than the open-loop gain of the op amp.

It can be shown that the cutoff frequency for the low-pass active
filter depicted in Figure 1–6(b) is given by the equation:

$$f_c = \frac{1}{2\pi RC} \tag{1-1}$$

where f_c is the frequency in Hz at which the output is −3 dB down

R is resistance in ohms

C is capacitance in farads, and $C_f = C$

Next, it is instructive to consider the single-loop, high-pass active filter depicted in Figure 1–7. Filter action takes place at the input circuit, where the incoming signal flows through a passive RC high-pass filter section and thence into the op amp. The R/10 series resistor serves to prevent overload of the op amp at very high frequencies owing to the decreasing reactance of capacitors C,C. Note that the op amp merely steps up the amplitude of the filter output in this example. In other words, the negative-feedback loop has no filter action (frequency discrimination). The negative-feedback resistor R_f functions to reduce the open-loop gain of the op amp, thereby contributing to operating stability. The cutoff frequency for the high-pass active filter depicted in Figure 1–6 is given by the equation:

$$f_c = \frac{1}{2\pi RC} \tag{1-2}$$

where f_c is the frequency in Hz at which the output is −3 dB down

C is capacitance in farads

R is resistance in ohms, and $R_f = R$

Although the high-pass active filter in Figure 1–7 is a very simple arrangement consisting of an RC passive filter section followed by a linear amplifier, it has some basic advantages over a passive filter alone. First, the op amp steps up the amplitude of the filter output, thereby eliminating an *insertion loss*. In other words, the passive RC filter section has an insertion loss which is equal to the difference between its input

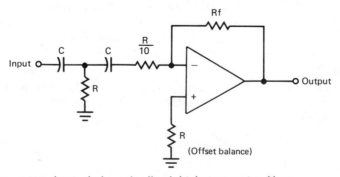

Fig. 1–7 A simple single-loop feedback high-pass active filter

signal power and its output signal power within the pass band. Insertion loss may be expressed in watt units or in dB units. Second, the op amp operates as a buffer between the output of the passive filter and the load at the op-amp output. This is an advantage, because the filter characteristics are not changed when the load impedance is changed. Third, the op amp provides a much lower output impedance than the passive-filter output impedance. This is an advantage because a comparatively large load current can be supplied.

1.6 BASIC BANDPASS AND NOTCH FILTERS

A bandpass filter attenuates frequencies on either side of its center frequency. Thus, a bandpass filter is formed by the overlapping responses of a low-pass filter and a high-pass filter. Figure 1–8 shows the arrangement for a basic single-loop feedback bandpass active filter. Note that this is a single-loop feedback configuration because there is only one negative-feedback signal returned to the input of the op amp. The passive low-pass RC feedback section comprises the R,R,2C circuit; the high-pass section comprises the C,C,R/2 circuit. Feedback is also provided through the 470-k resistor; it increases the bandwidth of the filter. Observe that if this resistor were replaced by a short-circuit, the

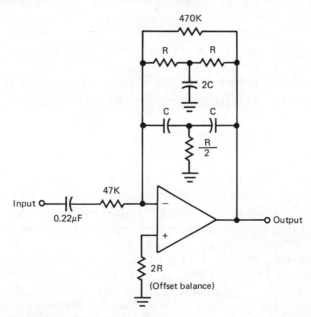

Fig. 1–8 A basic bandpass active filter.

passive RC filter sections would provide no frequency discrimination.

It is instructive to note that the feedback loop in Figure 1–8 by it-self has band-elimination action, or, it is a notch filter that provides trap action on an incoming signal. This combination of passive low-pass and high-pass RC filter sections is called a parallel-T RC filter, or a twin-T RC filter. With reference to Figure 1–9, the relative component values for zero signal transfer from input to output are given by the equations:

$$\omega^2 C_1 C_2 = 2/R_2^2 \tag{1-3}$$

$$\omega^2 C_1^2 = 1/(2R_1 R_2) \tag{1-4}$$

$$R_2 C_2 = 4R_1 C_1 \tag{1-5}$$

where resistance values are in ohms

capacitance values are in farads

$\omega = 2\pi f$ with f expressed in Hz

Zero transfer is obtained under these conditions, because the out-puts from the low-pass and high-pass sections have opposite phases and equal amplitudes at frequency f. If, as in Figure 1–8, we make $R_2 = 2R_1$ and $C_2 = 2C_1$, then the frequency of zero transfer is given by the equation:

$$f = 1/(2\pi C_1 R_2) = 1/(2\pi C_2 R_1) \tag{1-6}$$

With reference to the notation in Figure 1–8, the center frequency of the active bandpass filter is given by the equation:

$$f = \frac{1}{2\pi RC} \tag{1-7}$$

The arrangement shown in Figure 1–8 develops all of its useful frequency discrimination through the negative-feedback loop. In other words, there is no useful filter action provided by the input circuit. The input series capacitor and resistor merely prevent overload of the op amp at very high and very low frequencies.

Next, consider the action of the basic notch filter depicted in Fig-ure 1–9. In this example, the twin-T RC network used in the feedback loop of Figure 1–8 has been shifted to the input circuit of the op amp. Thus, this active filter consists of an RC passive filter section followed by a linear amplifier. In other words, the op amp provides no frequency

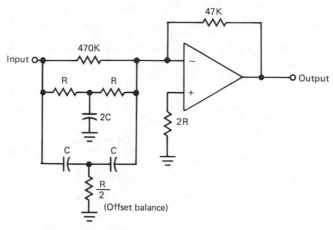

Fig. 1–9 A simple active notch filter.

discrimination, but merely steps up the output from the twin-T network. The 47-k feedback resistor reduces the open-loop gain of the op amp and stabilizes its operation. Since the same frequency-discriminating network is used in Figure 1–9 and Figure 1–8, the center frequency of the notch or trap characteristic is given by the preceding Equation (1–6). If the 470-k resistor is omitted in Figure 1–9, zero transfer is obtained at the notch frequency. Or, if the value of the 470-k resistor is reduced, the width of the rejection band is increased.

1.7 MULTILOOP FEEDBACK FILTERS

In addition to the basic single-loop feedback filters that have been noted, multiloop feedback filters are also used in many applications. These elaborated arrangements employ more than one op amp, as shown in the example of Figure 1–10. Each op amp has a negative-feedback loop, and the op amps are connected in cascade. Observe that the first op amp, OA1, has its input connected to two negative-feedback loops. Stage feedback occurs through R3, and overall feedback occurs through R2. The R3 feedback loop serves to reduce the open-loop gain and provides operating stability. On the other hand, the R2 feedback loop reduces the gain at low frequencies, because the third op amp, OA3, has low-pass output. Accordingly, high-pass output is obtained from OA1. Next, the second op amp has stage feedback through C, and therefore OA2 develops low-pass action. Note that the combination of OA1 highpass action and OA2 low-pass action results in bandpass action at the output of OA2. Finally, the third op amp has stage feedback through C

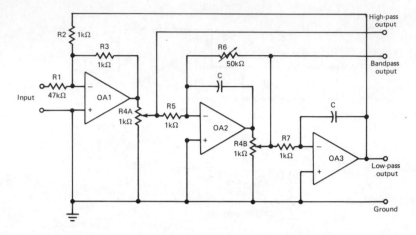

Fig. 1–10 A multiloop feedback active filter.

which provides additional low-pass action. Therefore, low-pass action is obtained from OA3.

The multiloop feedback active filter depicted in Figure 1–10 is also called a state variable filter. In other words, its frequency and selectivity can be adjusted independently. Thus, the value of R4A-B controls the bandpass frequency, and the value of R6 controls the bandwidth. A state variable filter has an advantage over simpler active filters in that it provides very sharp cutoff characteristics, with simultaneous high-pass, low-pass, and bandpass outputs. The bandpass center frequency of the configuration in Figure 1–10 is given by the equation:

$$f_c = \frac{k}{2\pi \times R4 \times C} \tag{1–8}$$

where f_c is the bandpass center frequency in Hz

> k varies between 0 and 1, depending on the setting of R4, with a value of 1 when OA2 drives OA3 directly, and OA2 drives OA3 directly
>
> R is resistance in ohms
>
> C is capacitance in farads

1.8 LOGARITHMIC AMPLIFIER

A logarithmic amplifier is a form of nonlinear amplifier which provides an output amplitude that is proportional to the logarithm of the input amplitude. It has no frequency discrimination. Logarithmic amplification is obtained with the basic arrangement shown in Figure 1–11. Nonlinear feedback is provided by a suitably biased power transistor operating in the common-base mode. Recall that the logarithm of one is zero, of 10 is one, of 100 is two, and so on. Thus, the 10-k offset null adjuster is set to zero the output of the op amp when one unit of positive signal is applied at the input terminal of the op amp. When larger values of positive input signals are applied, the transistor automatically feeds back a disproportionate amount of voltage and the output is precisely proportional to the logarithm of the input amplitude. Of course, a logarithmic amplifier cannot provide a precise output level if operated out of its rated input-voltage range.

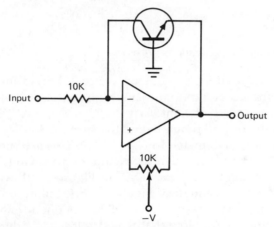

Fig. 1–11 Basic logarithmic amplifier arrangement.

1.9 BASIC TROUBLESHOOTING APPROACH

Troubleshooting of op-amp arrangements starts with symptom analysis. It is helpful to evaluate trouble symptoms with respect to a block diagram, because the various blocks have functional relationships. In turn, the particular malfunction may indicate that there is a defective component in a certain block. Thereby, preliminary localization of the fault is determined. As an illustration, consider the block diagram of the biquadratic bandpass filter shown in Figure 1–12. It is evident that if the functions of the three blocks are known, a trouble symptom can be evaluated from the viewpoint of preliminary localization. Therefore, the troubleshooter needs to know the overall function and the various subfunctions of the op-amp arrangement with which he is concerned.

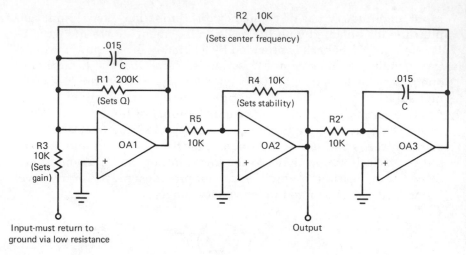

Fig. 1–12   An op-amp biquadratic bandpass section.

Otherwise, he must adopt a "shotgun" approach, and merely replace various components at random. This approach is usually wasteful, time-consuming, and inefficient.

Consider the overall function and the subfunctions of the biquadratic bandpass section depicted in Figure 1–12. This is basically a multiloop feedback active filter, such as exemplified previously in Figure 1–10. If we interchange OA1 and OA2 in Figure 1–10, we obtain the biquadratic filter arrangement of Figure 1–12. It follows from previous discussion also that bandpass output will be obtained from OA2 in the biquadratic arrangement. Note that the term *biquadratic* means merely that the filter action is described by an algebraic equation of the fourth degree. This bandpass filter is equivalent to a simple RLC series circuit, as pictured in Figure 1–13. Note that the bandwidth of the filter depends upon the Q value of the circuit. Since the Q value is determined by R1 in Figure 1–12, it follows that if the 0.015-μF capacitor in shunt to R1 becomes leaky, the selectivity of the filter will become subnormal. Therefore, this is the first possibility that the troubleshooter would investigate if a symptom of poor selectivity occurs.

On the other hand, consider the malfunction that results in case the foregoing capacitor becomes open-circuited. In such a case, the OA1 block does not develop low-pass action, and therefore, bandpass output is not obtained from OA2. Since the filter action of OA3 is unchanged in this example, feedback via R2 produces high-pass response, and high-pass output is obtained from OA2. Accordingly, if a trouble symptom of high-pass output occurs, instead of bandpass output, the troubleshooter would proceed to check the possibility of an open feedback ca-

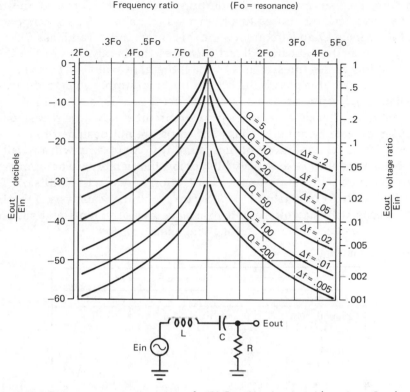

Fig. 1–13 Frequency response curves for RLC series circuits with various Q values.

pacitor in the OA1 section. Although other component defects can occur, capacitor defects are more common than resistor faults or op-amp malfunctions. Therefore, a troubleshooter checks out possible capacitor defects first. Note that a suspected "open" capacitor can be checked simply by "bridging" it temporarily with a known good capacitor. Then, if the system action is restored to normal, the diagnosis is confirmed.

Next, consider the trouble symptom that results in case the feedback capacitor in the OA3 section (Figure 1–12) becomes "open". In such a case, there is no low-pass feedback to OA1, and the system does not develop high-pass action. However, OA1 continues to develop low-pass action, and low-pass output is obtained from OA2. Accordingly, if a trouble symptom of low-pass output occurs, instead of bandpass output, the troubleshooter would proceed to check the possibility of an open feedback capacitor in the OA3 section. Again, suppose that this feedback capacitor becomes leaky. In this situation, the effective capacitance value is reduced and the cutoff frequency of the stage is increased.

In turn, the bandwidth of the output from OA2 is increased and the center frequency is shifted to a higher value. Table 1–1 lists component values versus Q and frequency for this biquadratic bandpass filter. It follows that if a capacitor defect increases the bandwidth of the OA2 output (decreases the system Q value), the gain will also decrease.

Other trouble possibilities are subnormal supply voltage, off-value resistors, defective op amps, cracked circuit boards, and cold-soldered connections. Leakage between printed-circuit conductors occasionally causes trouble symptoms. Many op amps are not designed to operate normally under conditions of high humidity. An op amp will also fail to operate normally at excessively high or low temperatures. For example, a typical op amp is rated for normal operation between the limits of $-55°$ and $125°C$. It is often helpful to follow up preliminary analysis of trouble symptoms with dc voltage and resistance measurements and suitable system tests, as explained in following chapters.

TABLE 1–1

Component values versus Q and Frequency			
Frequency	C	Q	R1
10 Hz	15 μF	0.5	5 K
20 Hz	7.5 μF	1	10 K
50 Hz	3.3 μF	2	20 K
100 Hz	1.5 μF	5	50 K
200 Hz	.75 μF	10	100 K
500 Hz	.33 μF	20	200 K
1 kHz	.0159 μF	50	510 K*
2 kHz	7500 pF	100	1.2 meg*
5 kHz	3300 pF	200	3.3 meg*
10 kHz	1500 pF	500	10 meg*
(values approximate—rounded to stock sizes)		(values approximate—*influenced by frequency and supply voltage)	
If R3 = 10 K, circuit gain = Q If R3 = 100 K, circuit gain = Q/10 If R3 = 1 K, circuit gain = 10 Q etc...			

Catastrophic destruction of an op amp usually occurs if the power-supply polarity is accidentally reversed. Therefore, protective diodes may be included in series with the power-supply leads, as depicted in Figure 1–14. This is the most common arrangement. However, protective diodes may be utilized also in configurations that have a single power supply with a resistive divider, or a single power supply with a zener-diode regulator, as shown in Fig. 1–15. Diode protection is

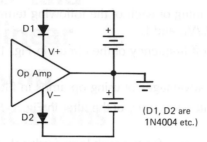

Fig. 1–14   D1 and D2 function as protective diodes.

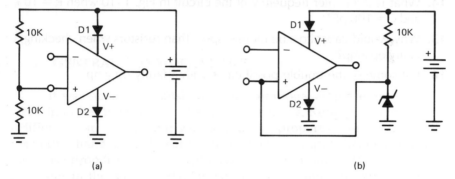

(a)   (b)

Fig. 1–15   Other protective-diode arrangements. **(a)** For single power source with resistive divider; **(b)** For single power source with zener-diode regulator.

most advantageous in battery-powered equipment, because inexperienced personnel can become confused concerning correct polarity relations.

REVIEW QUESTIONS

1. What is the circuit called when both inputs of an op amp are driven?
2. What is the deviation from zero called?
3. What is a voltage follower circuit?
4. What is one important advantage of differential amplifier operation?
5. How is an operational amplifier kept from oscillating?
6. What is a limiter?
7. In Fig. 1–6(b), what effect does C_f have on the cutoff frequency?

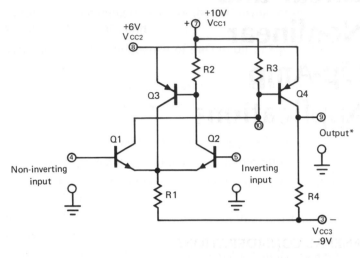

Notes: Pin 10 is for frequency shaping
         Pins 1, 2, and 6 - no internal connection

         *Output offset voltage = −0.5V

Fig. 2–1   A simple operational-amplifier configuration.

amp is 62 dB, it follows that the input signal amplitude must not exceed 2.5 mV if the linear dynamic range is not to be exceeded. However, suppose that an input signal amplitude of 5 mV is applied. In such a case, Q1 and Q2 will be driven into nonlinear regions of operation, and the input signal will not be amplified linearly. Instead, the driving signal to Q4 will be compressed or clipped on its positive and negative peaks. Positive-peak clipping results from driving one input transistor into saturation, and negative-peak clipping results from driving the other input transistor into saturation.

Note in passing that the op amp depicted in Figure 2–1 has an input resistance of approximately 10,000 ohms and an output resistance of about 10 ohms. As noted previously, an ideal op amp would have no output offset voltage. In other words, the resting dc output voltage would have the same value as the resting dc voltage at the input. However, in a simple arrangement such as Figure 2–1, there is considerable dc offset voltage at the output. That is, when the inverting and the non-inverting input terminals are grounded through 510-ohm resistors, and the output terminal works into an open circuit, there is a dc offset voltage of −0.5 volt between the output terminal and either of the input terminals. Although this would be a serious problem in some applications, a large offset voltage is of no concern in arrangements that do not employ a negative-feedback loop.

2.2 APPLICATION NOTES

It is instructive to consider the linear op-amp applications shown in Figure 2–2. Observe that a subtracter is arranged so that one voltage is applied to the inverting input of the op amp, and another voltage is applied to the noninverting input. In turn, the voltages tend to cancel each other out, and the difference appears as the output voltage e_3. Note that the input voltages e_1 and e_2 must have the same polarity. Either dc or ac input voltages may be utilized; in other words, both e_1 and e_2 may be dc voltages, or both may be ac voltages. Note that the subtracter will not function, however, if e_1 is a dc voltage and e_2 is an ac voltage. In case e_1 and e_2 are ac voltages, they must have the same frequency and phase. That is, if e_1 and e_2 were ac voltages with a random or unknown phase relation, the amplitude of the output voltage e_3 would have an unknown relation to the amplitudes of e_1 and e_2.

Next, consider the adder/subtracter arrangement depicted in Figure 2–2(b). This will be recognized as a combination of the adder configuration that was explained in Chapter 1, and of the subtracter configuration described above. Note that all four input voltages must have the same polarity in an adder/subtracter arrangement. Either ac or dc voltages may be employed. In ac operation, all the input voltages must have the same frequency and phase. Note also that the operating frequency must not exceed the rated frequency capability of the op amp. As an illustration, a typical op amp has a rated frequency response from dc to 50 kHz. If operation were attempted at a frequency greater than 50 kHz, subnormal amplification would result and the balance between inverting and noninverting functions would tend to become upset.

It is instructive to consider briefly how voltages add in a resistive adder circuit. As an illustration, we will observe how voltage e_1 is added to voltage e_2 in Figure 2–2(b). To reduce the circuit to its essential functional form, refer to Figure 2–3(a). Note that e_1 and e_2 are basically constant-voltage sources; in other words, the internal resistance of these two sources is considered to be zero. The output voltage e_3 is the drop across the lower resistor R. Now, let us stipulate that the source e_2 has a value of zero, and that the source e_1 has a value of E volts. In turn, source e_2 can be replaced by a short-circuit, and we obtain the equivalent circuit shown in Figure 2–3(b). It is evident by inspection that the output voltage will be equal to 1/3E. Next, let us stipulate that source e_1 and source e_2 each has a value of E volts. In turn, we obtain the equivalent circuit depicted in Figure 2–3(c). It is apparent that both of the input currents produce an output voltage drop. Finally, the output voltage will be equal to 2/3E. Hint: In case this value is not self-evident, the student may apply Ohm's law and Kirchhoff's current law to the circuit.

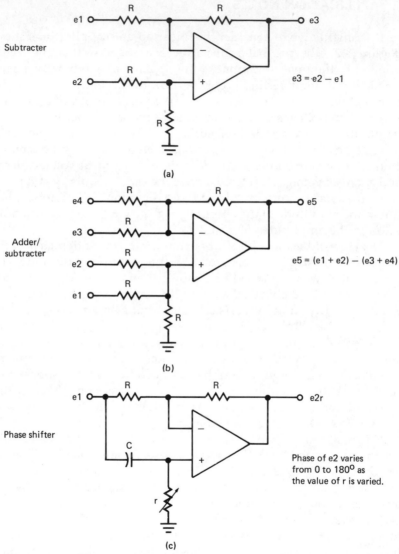

Fig. 2–2 Typical linear op-amp applications.

Next, consider the phase-shifter op-amp arrangement shown in Figure 2–2(c). This is, in the first analysis, a subtracter configuration in which the inverting and noninverting inputs are energized through dividers from the same ac source. However, a variable resistance is included in the divider circuit to the noninverting input. This variable resistance provides an adjustable phase shift of the voltage applied to the noninverting input. Note that the voltage applied to the inverting

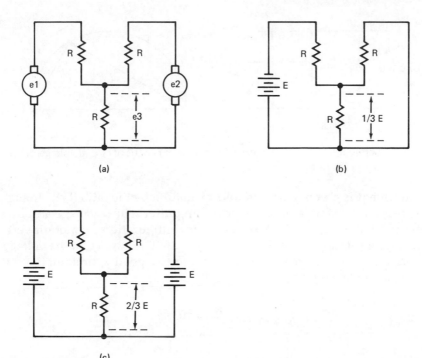

(a)

(b)

(c)

Fig. 2–3 Example of resistive adder action. **(a)** Equivalent circuit; **(b)** Source e_1 equal to E, and source e_2 equal to zero; **(c)** Source e_1 and source e_2 both equal to E.

input has a fixed phase. In turn, the phase of the output voltage e_2 depends upon the vector difference of the two input voltages. Variation of the value of r can provide a phase variation range of practically 180°. The basis of this phase variation is shown in Figure 2–4. This semicircle diagram depicts the locus of voltage e_r as the value of r is varied. The phase angle between e_r and e_1 is ϕ. Note that when r has a very small value, ϕ approaches 90°; on the other hand, when r has a very large value, ϕ approaches 0°.

It is helpful to observe op-amp characteristics and differential-amplifier function in somewhat greater detail at this point. With reference to the subtracter configuration depicted in Figure 2–2(a), inverting-amplifier and noninverting-amplifier functions are employed. The gain of the basic inverting-amplifier arrangement was noted in Chapter 1. It might be supposed that the gain of the basic noninverting-amplifier arrangement is identical. However, this is not quite correct. Refer to Figure 2–5. The basic configuration for an inverting amplifier is shown in Figure 2–5(a). As noted in Chapter 1, the voltage amplification of the

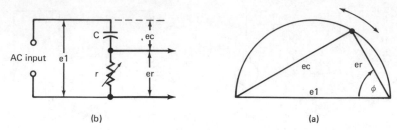

Fig. 2–4 Semicircle diagram for series RC circuit. **(a)** Locus of circuit voltage drops; **(b)** Reference circuit.

arrangement is given to a good approximation by the ratio R_f/R_i. In Figure 2–5(b) an example of an inverting amplifier with a voltage amplification of 100 is depicted. Next, the basic configuration for a noninverting amplifier is shown in Figure 2–4(c). It can be shown that the voltage amplification of this arrangement is given to a good approximation by the equation:

$$A = \frac{R_i + R_f}{R_i} \tag{2-1}$$

In Figure 2–4(d) an example of a noninverting amplifier with the same resistive values as in Figure 2–5(b) is depicted. Note that in this example the voltage amplification is 101 times. In other words, the noninverting arrangement has 1 per cent greater gain than the inverting arrangement. Thus, a subtracter designed from basic op-amp circuitry would have an inherent error of 1 per cent. However, note that this error is easily avoided by driving the noninverting input through a resistive voltage divider that imposes a 1 per cent loss on the input signal amplitude.

2.3 INPUT AND OUTPUT RESISTANCE CHARACTERISTICS

The input resistance and output resistance of an op amp is determined by its internal design. However, the input resistance of an op-amp stage may be quite different from the input resistance of the op amp itself. Similarly, the output resistance of the stage might be different from the output resistance of the op amp itself. In other words, the input and output circuitry that is employed may be the determining factor. As an illustration, Figure 2–6 shows the input and feedback signal currents for basic inverting and noninverting amplifiers. Applica-

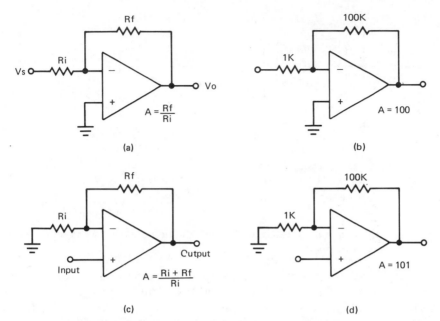

Fig. 2–5 Inverting and noninverting amplifier arrangements. **(a)** Basic inverting amplifier configuration; **(b)** Example of stage amplification; **(c)** Basic noninverting amplifier configuration; **(d)** Comparative example of stage amplification.

tion of a signal voltage V_s causes an input current flow I_i in Figure 2–6(a). Since the op amp has extremely high gain, the feedback current I_f is almost as large as I_i. From the viewpoint of input-resistance analysis, we may assume that I_f is equal to I_i. In turn, the inverting-input $(-)$ terminal of the op amp is practically at zero potential. This means that the inverting-input terminal "looks like" a ground point to the input signal. Or, the input resistance to the inverting op-amp arrangement is practically equal to R_1.

Next, consider the input resistance of the noninverting op-amp arrangement depicted in Figure 2–6(b). As before, I_f is almost equal to I_i. However, the two currents do not oppose in this amplifier configuration. Therefore, the input resistance to the noninverting op-amp terminal $(+)$ is determined essentially by the internal design of the op amp. A typical high-performance op amp will present an input resistance of less than one megohm up to several hundred megohms. Note that the input resistance of an op amp basically denotes the ratio of input voltage to input current. With reference to Figure 2–6(a), the input resistance is accordingly equal to V_s/I_i. Observe that I_i is given by the ratio of the voltage drop across R_1 to the resistance of R_1. Since the signal volt-

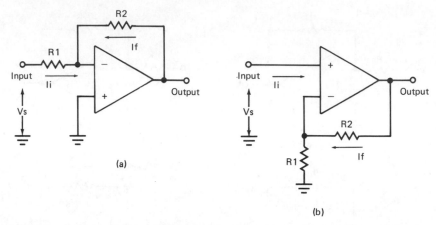

Fig. 2–6 Analysis of input resistance. **(a)** Inverting op-amp arrangement; **(b)** Noninverting op-amp arrangement.

age at the inverting terminal of the op amp is practically zero, the voltage drop across R_1 is equal to V_s, and the input current I_i is equal to V_s/R_1. In turn, the input resistance is equal to V_s divided by V_s/R_1, or the input resistance is equal to R_1. Next, with reference to Figure 2–6(b), the input current at the noninverting terminal of the op amp is typically 2.5 μA at 1V, or the input resistance is equal to 0.4 megohm.

Consider next the output resistance of an op amp, apart from its load circuitry. Just as variously designed op amps may have inherent (intrinsic) input resistances as low as several thousand ohms or as high as several hundred megohms, so do inherent output resistances vary. As an illustration, a typical high-performance op amp may have an output resistance of 150 ohms. Another op amp may have an output resistance of 75 ohms. A very simple design might have an output resistance of 10,000 ohms. The comparatively simple design depicted in Figure 2–7 has a rated output resistance of 160 ohms. Typical op amps can provide an output voltage swing of 6 volts peak-to-peak. If a reduction in output-voltage swing is permissible in a particular application, the output can be taken from a voltage divider connected to the output terminal of the op amp. In turn the output resistance of the op-amp stage will be less than the inherent output resistance of the op amp itself.

2.4 BASIC NONLINEAR RESPONSES

A typical op amp is rated for a maximum signal-output current of 25 milliamperes. To protect the op amp from possible damage, a current limiter or clamper may be built into the output stage. In such a case, the

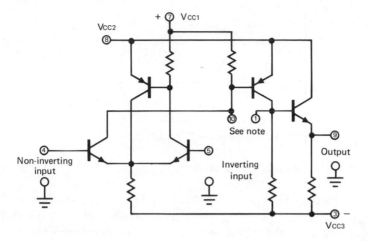

Notes: Pins 10 and 1 are for frequency shaping
Pins 2 and 6 - no internal connection

Fig. 2–7 A simple op-amp configuration with a rated output resistance of 1,600 ohms.

output waveform will be clipped if the output-current demand is exceeded. Figure 2–8 depicts an example of current clipping, or current limiting distortion. Next, consider the effect of voltage clipping distortion. Voltage clipping results from limiting of the maximum output voltage capability for the op amp. For example, a typical op amp has an output voltage capability approximately one volt less than the power-supply voltages. In case the op amp is driven beyond its output-voltage capability, the output waveform will become clipped. Clipping occurs on both positive and negative peaks, as depicted in Figure 2–8.

As noted previously, it is also possible to overdrive the input section of an op amp. The input voltage limits are often determined for positive inputs by saturation of the input transistors, and for negative inputs by saturation of the current source transistor. If the positive input limit is exceeded, the op amp may be damaged. Or, if the input transistors are not damaged, a condition called latch-up or "stuck at" response may occur. For example, if the transistor at the inverting input saturates, it no longer functions as an inverting amplifier, but provides a current path between the input terminal and the base of the second input transistor. Thus, the inverting input is changed by overdrive into a noninverting input. Under this condition, the negative-feedback voltage acts as a positive-feedback voltage, and the output voltage may hold the input stage in saturation. This is the latch-up type of nonlinear response.

Latch-up response is more likely to occur in a voltage-follower arrangement than in amplifier configurations that employ less negative

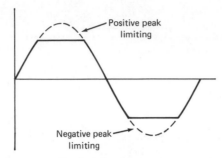

Fig. 2–8 Example of current clipping distortion.

feedback. As seen in Figure 2–9(a), the output from the op amp is directly connected to the inverting input in a voltage follower. If a transient voltage occurs in the input and momentarily overdrives the input section of the op amp, latch-up is almost certain to result. Sometimes a 33-k resistor is connected in series with the feedback loop to limit the negative-feedback voltage. However, this method of preventing latch-up results in an increase of offset voltage. A somewhat more sophisticated method of avoiding latch-up in a voltage follower is depicted in Figure 2–9(b). A diode clamp D_1 is utilized to limit the amplitude of feedback voltage and thereby to prevent the input transistor of the op amp from going into saturation. Note that an input series resistor R_1 is also provided. This resistor might have a value of 10 k, and provides limiting of input transients without increasing the offset voltage excessively.

Various other protective circuitry is used in voltage-follower arrangements, as explained in greater detail subsequently. Note in passing that the input resistance of a voltage follower is very high, and the output resistance is very low. The voltage gain is practically unity. A voltage follower is employed for impedance transformation and/or

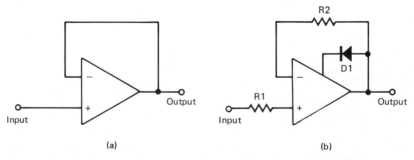

Fig. 2–9 Latch-up protection in the voltage follower. **(a)** Basic follower arrangement; **(b)** Latch-up protection by series resistance and diode clamping.

sectional isolation in most applications. A typical input resistance of 30 megohms can be obtained with suitable circuitry, and an input resistance of 15 megohms is provided with circuitry that is optimized for dc balance. The output impedance provided by a voltage follower is considerably lower than the output impedance of an emitter follower because of the extremely high gain of an op amp in comparison to the gain of a transistor.

2.5 BIAS CURRENT OFFSET CONSIDERATIONS

In both linear and nonlinear applications, consideration of bias current offset is generally of basic importance. As noted previously, an ideal op amp would have zero output voltage when the input voltage is zero. In practice, however, this may not be the case. The output voltage that is present when the input voltage is zero is called the output offset voltage. This output offset voltage, of course, is fed back to the inverting input of the op amp through the feedback loop. In turn, the circuit action may be disturbed. Note that there are two basic causes of output offset voltage: input bias current and input offset voltage. We will consider the characteristics of input bias currents and their control at this point, and then proceed to the problem of input offset voltage and output offset null adjustment.

All op amps have differential-amplifier input stages. A differential amplifier is so-called because it amplifies the difference between two input signals (the signal at the inverting input and the signal at the noninverting input). With reference to Figure 2–10, the current-source transistor Q3 provides a practical constant-current supply to transistors Q1 and Q2. To briefly review the basic semiconductor theory that is involved here, the current that flows from the emitter to the collector of a transistor is determined by the base bias current times the beta value of the transistor. Moreover, the value of this emitter-to-collector current is practically independent of the emitter-collector voltage. In other words, the emitter-collector current that flows through Q3 is essentially constant, because this current depends only on the fixed value of base-bias current I_{BQ3}.

Both of the inputs to the differential amplifier have been placed at ground potential in Figure 2–10. It is evident that one-half of I_{CQ3} will flow through Q1, and that the other half will flow through Q2. Each of these currents is related to the base-bias currents of Q1 and Q2. In other words, I_{CQ1} is equal to beta times I_{BQ1}, and I_{CQ2} is equal to beta times I_{BQ2}. The base-bias currents I_{BQ1} and I_{BQ2} are called the input bias currents.

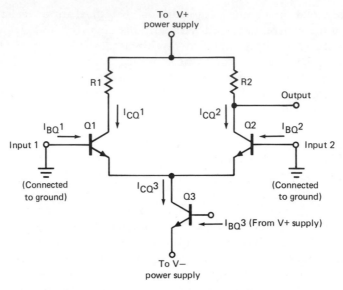

Fig. 2–10   Basic differential-amplifier configuration with a constant-current source.

Note that the output is taken from the collector of Q2. Now, suppose that I_{BQ1} and I_{BQ2} are both increased by the same amount (Figure 2–11). This increase is called a common-mode input signal. The common-mode signal would cause an increase in I_{CQ1} and I_{CQ2} if Q3 were not present. However, the presence of Q3 prevents any change in total current. Therefore, the output of the differential amplifier remains unchanged. The only change that does occur is an increase in the collector-emitter voltage of Q3.

To repeat a basic principle, the output of a differential amplifier is unaffected by application of a common-mode input signal. Next, consider the result of applying a differential-mode input signal (Figure 2–12). Note that a positive voltage is applied to Input 1, and a negative voltage is applied to Input 2. In turn, I_{BQ1} increases, and I_{BQ2} decreases. Similarly, I_{CQ1} increases, and I_{CQ2} decreases. Of course, the sum of the collector currents remains unchanged, because of the constant-current action of Q3. Since I_{CQ2} decreases, the voltage drop across R2 decreases, and there is a corresponding change in output voltage. In practice, it is not possible to match the components perfectly and to maintain I_{CQ3} absolutely constant. A typical op amp will amplify a differential-mode signal approximately 10,000 times more than it will amplify a common-mode signal. Therefore, in the majority of practical applications, it can be assumed that the op amp does not respond to common-mode signals.

In this discussion of bias-current offset, we will define input bias currents as those currents that must be supplied at the input terminals

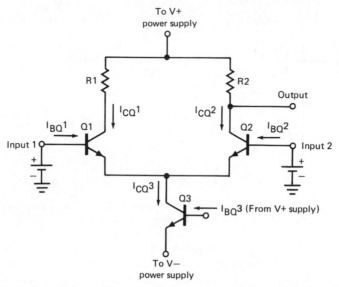

Fig. 2–11 Differential amplifier with a common-mode input signal applied.

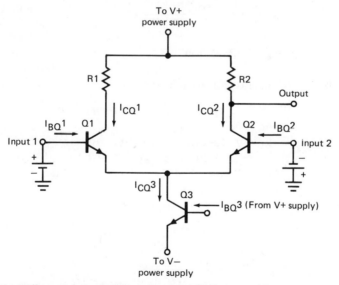

Fig. 2–12 Differential-mode input signal applied to amplifier.

of an op amp to provide correct biasing of the differential input-stage transistors. With reference to Figure 2–13(a), the input bias current flows through R1 and R2 to the output terminal and thence through the load to ground. This input bias current develops a voltage drop across R1 and R2, and appears as an input voltage at the inverting terminal of

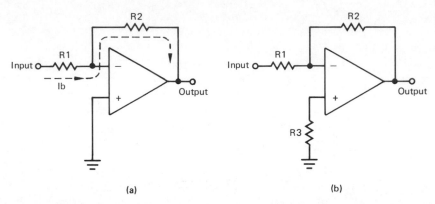

Fig. 2–13 Input bias-current considerations. **(a)** Path of input bias current; **(b)** Insertion of bias-current balancing resistor.

the op amp. This is a differential input voltage, since there is no corresponding voltage applied at the noninverting terminal. Therefore, the input bias current is amplified by the op amp, and the resulting output offset voltage is given approximately by the equation:

$$E_{os} = I_b R_2 \qquad (2\text{--}2)$$

where E_{os} is the output offset voltage

I_b is the input bias current

R2 is the negative-feedback resistance

As noted previously, the output offset voltage owing to input bias current through the feedback loop can be cancelled out by insertion of a suitable resistance between the noninverting input terminal and ground (R3 in Figure 2–13(b)). The value of R3 is chosen to develop a voltage drop equal to $I_b R2$, and this required value is given by the equation:

$$R3 = \frac{R1 \times R2}{R1 + R2} \qquad (2\text{--}3)$$

where R1 and R2 have the significance indicated in Figure 2–13(a).

It was also noted previously that perfect op amps cannot be designed and manufactured, with the result that even when the input bias current is cancelled out, there is generally a small output offset voltage remaining. To bring the output terminal of the op amp to zero potential, R3 must usually be adjusted to provide an input bias current slightly

greater or slightly less than the input bias current at the inverting terminal of the op amp. The difference between these two input bias currents is called the input offset current. Note that the output offset voltage produced by the input offset current is given approximately by the
equation:

$$E_{os} = I_{os}R2 \qquad\qquad (2\text{--}4)$$

where E_{os} is the output offset voltage

I_{os} is the input offset current

R2 is the negative-feedback resistance

Next, consider the characteristics of input offset voltage. With reference to Figure 2–14(a), an input offset voltage is defined as the differential input voltage that must be applied to the input terminals of an
op amp to bring the output terminal to zero potential. An ideal op amp
would have zero input offset voltage. In practice, however, the input
offset voltage is not quite zero, owing to tolerances on the internal components of the op amp. The input offset voltage can be represented as
a small voltage source in series with the noninverting input terminal of
the op amp, as depicted in Figure 2–14(b). In turn, the output offset voltage that results from the input offset voltage is given by the equation:

$$E_{os} = \frac{R1 + R2}{R1} \times V_{os} \qquad\qquad (2\text{--}5)$$

where E_{os} is the output offset voltage

V_{os} is the input offset voltage

R1 is the resistance of the input component

R2 is the resistance of the feedback component

A typical high-performance op amp is rated for a maximum input
bias current of 80 nA (8×10^{-9} ampere), a maximum input offset current
of 20 nA, and a maximum input offset voltage of 1 mV (10^{-3} volt). Substitution in the foregoing equations shows that the corresponding output offsets owing to input bias current and input offset voltage are 0.8
mV and 101 mV, assuming that R1 = 100 ohms, and R2 = 10 k. Since the
output offset voltages are caused by tolerances on different components
in the op amp, the two voltages may have either polarity (may add or

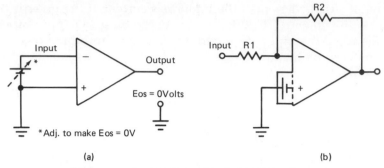

Fig. 2–14 Representation of input offset voltage. **(a)** Input offset voltage represented as an external battery; **(b)** Input offset voltage represented as an internal battery.

subtract). In case they happen to add, the total output offset voltage would be 101.8 mV in this example. As a practical application note, this total output offset would not be regarded as serious. However, if a balancing resistor is inserted (R3 in Figure 2–13(b)), the value of output offset voltage owing to bias current can be substantially reduced. As noted previously, in case the total output offset voltage must be exactly zero, a null potentiometer is included in the input configuration.

2.6 TROUBLESHOOTING TECHNIQUES

DC voltage and resistance measurements are basic in troubleshooting op-amp systems. Some op amp circuits have very high internal impedance. As an illustration, two amplifier circuits are depicted in Figure 2–15. One circuit has a gain of 100 times, and the other circuit has a gain of two times. The low-gain amplifier has some very high internal impedances. Note that the inverting input is connected to a 5-meg resistor and a 10-meg resistor. Also, the noninverting input is connected to a 3.3-meg resistor. Because these input circuits have such a high value of internal resistance, it would be impossible to measure the input offset voltage with a 20,000 ohms-per-volt VOM. A conventional VOM will load the circuits excessively and the voltage readings will be meaningless. Instead, it is necessary to employ a TVM that has an input resistance of at least 10 megohms. For example, an FET multimeter such as illustrated in Figure 2–16 is suitable.

Note that the instrument shown in Figure 2–16 has a hi-lo ohmmeter function. When operated in its hi-pwr mode, conventional ohmmeter action is provided. In other words, the ohmmeter is energized by a 1.5-volt battery. On the other hand, when the ohmmeter is operated

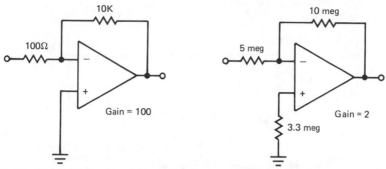

Fig. 2–15 Op-amp circuits with voltages of 100 and of 2.

Fig. 2–16 A hi-lo FET multimeter. *(Courtesy, Sencore)*

in its lo-pwr mode, the instrument applies a maximum of 0.08 volt across the circuit under test. This feature ensures that semiconductor junctions will not be "turned on" during in-circuit resistance measurements. To understand the advantage of low-voltage ohmmeter testing in semiconductor circuits, refer to Figure 2–17. This is a simple inverting-amplifier configuration. To measure resistance values, the 15-volt sup-

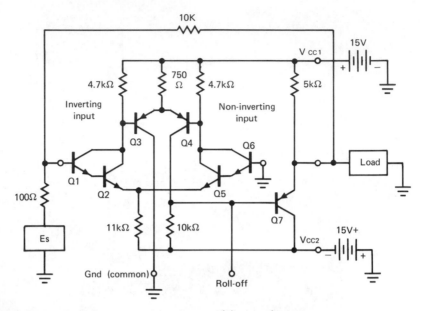

Fig. 2–17 A simple op-amp inverting-amplifier configuration.

plies must be disconnected and the input voltage E_s switched off. Then, the values of the 100-ohm resistor, the 10-k feedback resistor, and the load resistance can be measured in-circuit with a lo-pwr ohmmeter. In other words, none of the transistor junctions can be turned on by a test voltage of 0.08 volt, or less.

Of course, the foregoing conclusion is based on the assumption that the op amp is not defective. As an illustration, if the collector junction of Q1 happens to be short-circuited (Figure 2–17), a lo-pwr ohmmeter will not indicate the correct resistance of the 10-k feedback resistor on an in-circuit test. Note that in this situation, the 10-k resistor would be effectively shunted by a 4.7-k resistor in series with a 5-k resistor. In turn, the ohmmeter would indicate a resistance of approximately 5 k. In such a case, the technician would disconnect the 10-k feedback resistor from the op amp, and measure its resistance out-of-circuit. The result, of course, would be that the 10-k resistor would now measure its normal value. In turn, the logical conclusion would be that the op amp is defective. It is instructive to note in passing that the input transistors Q1 and Q2, and Q5 and Q6 are Darlington-connected. This connection is used to obtain comparatively high input impedance — typically 1 megohm.

A test oscillator is also a basic instrument in troubleshooting of op-amp systems. Figure 2–18 illustrates a suitable high-quality test oscillator. It is used to inject sine-wave signals at various points. Since

Fig. 2–18 A high-quality test oscillator. *(Courtesy, Hewlett-Packard)*

a wide range of test voltages are needed in general troubleshooting procedures, a test oscillator should provide an output signal range from 0.1 mV to several volts. A calibrated attenuator is not a necessity, although it can often simplify test procedures and reduce the number of voltage measurements that are required. In some situations, the frequency response of an op-amp section or system may need to be measured. Accordingly, the test oscillator should provide an ample frequency range. For example, the instrument shown in Figure 2–18 has a frequency range from 5 Hz to 1.2 MHz. Although high-fidelity response is seldom required in op-amp systems, it is nevertheless desirable to employ a test oscillator with a comparatively low percentage of distortion. The instrument in Figure 2–18 is rated for a harmonic distortion of less than 0.1% from 30 Hz to 100 kHz, less than 0.6% from 5 Hz to 30 Hz, and less than 1% from 100 kHz to 1.2 MHz.

Tests of op-amp response in comparator arrangements are often facilitated by the availability of a square-wave generator and an oscilloscope. These instruments are employed, for example, to measure the slew rate of the op amp. The slew rate is defined as the maximum rate of change (maximum speed of response) to an input signal that suddenly changes from a maximum positive value to a maximum negative value. This topic is discussed in greater detail subsequently. A typical high-performance op amp is rated for a slew rate of 0.5 volt per microsecond. Accordingly, a suitable square-wave generator should have a rise time (Figure 2–19) of much less than 1 microsecond. The instrument illustrated in Figure 2–20 has a rated rise time of 50 nanoseconds (50 ns). It has a frequency range from 4 Hz to 2 MHz, with a maximum output of 5 volts which can be attenuated 80 dB.

A companion oscilloscope suitable for slew-rate testing is illustrated in Figure 2–21. This instrument has a vertical-amplifier bandwidth from dc to 15 MHz, and two time bases. The second time base functions as a delay generator, so that a signal that is related to an initiating signal, but delayed in time, can be easily displayed. A calibrated delay range from 2 μs to 10 s is provided. Time base A is adjustable from 0.1 μs/cm to 5 s/cm in 24 calibrated steps. Time base B is adjustable from 2 μs/cm to 1 s/cm, in 18 calibrated steps. It is useful as a repetition-rate generator over the range of 0.1 Hz to 40 kHz. A sweep magnifier of 5X extends the maximum sweep speed to 20 ns/cm. Expertise in oscilloscope testing procedures requires both specialized study and practical experience.

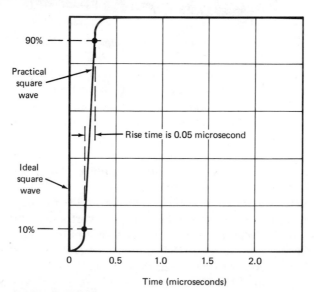

Fig. 2–19 Measurement of rise time.

Fig. 2–20 A high-performance square-wave generator. *(Courtesy, Hewlett-Packard)*

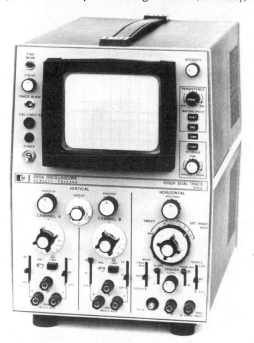

Fig. 2–21 A triggered-sweep oscilloscope with calibrated time base. *(Courtesy, Hewlett-Packard)*

REVIEW QUESTIONS

1. What is the difference between a linear and nonlinear mode of operation?

2. In Fig. 2–1, what is the function of Q3?

3. Compare the input resistance of the circuit in Fig. 2–1 to the output resistance.

4. Why isn't the 0.5 volt dc offset voltage in Fig. 2–1 a problem?

5. What is the requirement of the input voltages in Fig. 2–2?

6. What is the frequency requirement of the adder/subtracter in Fig. 2–2 (b)?

7. What is the voltage amplification of the circuit in Fig. 2–5(b) when $R_i = 10k$ ohms and $R_p = 1M$ ohm?

8. What is the value of the input resistance of the inverting terminal of the circuit configuration in Fig. 2–6(a)?

9. What is the range of input resistance values of typical op amps?

10. What can we state about the value of the output resistance of an op amp circuit?

11. Other than the internal construction of the op amp, what limits the voltage swing of an op amp circuit?

12. What is latch-up?

13. What is the problem that results when the circuit in Fig. 2–9(a) is used to prevent latch-up?

14. Why is the output resistance of a voltage follower less than that of an emitter follower?

15. What is a differential amplifier?

16. In Fig. 2–13(a) what is the value of the output offset voltage when I_b is $20\mu A$ and R_2 is 100k ohms?

17. Why should you use a TVM to measure the dc voltage of most op amps?

18. Why is it necessary to use a Lo-Pwr ohmmeter to measure resistance in an op amp circuit?

19. Define the term "slew rate" as it applies to an op amp.

3 · Inductance Simulation by Operational Amplifiers

3.1 GENERAL CONSIDERATIONS

Transistors, diodes, resistors, and capacitors are built into integrated circuits. On the other hand, inductors as such cannot be formed in IC technology. Therefore, various expedients are employed to simulate inductance in IC packages by means of suitable configurations of capacitors, resistors, and op amps. At this point, it is instructive to briefly review the basic characteristics of inductors and capacitors. With reference to Figure 3–1, an ideal or pure inductor is a *two-terminal device* consisting essentially of a coil of wire wound in the form of a spiral or helix. This ideal inductor has an electrical property called inductance, and the wire is assumed to have zero resistance. It is also assumed that the ideal inductor has no distributed capacitance (no capacitance between consecutive turns of wire). The property of inductance can be compared to the inertia of a flywheel. In other words, a flywheel opposes the driving force that tends to speed up its rotation. Once the flywheel has been placed in rotation, it opposes the braking force that tends to slow down its rotation. Similarly, an inductor opposes current buildup when a voltage is applied to the terminals of the coil; conversely, the inductor opposes current decay when the voltage is switched off.

Note that the foregoing flywheel and inductor characteristics are based on energy storage. In other words, a flywheel stores mechanical energy as its speed of rotation increases. An inductor stores electrical energy as the current through its winding increases. It is apparent that an ideal flywheel or an ideal inductor does not convert ("use up") energy, but merely holds its stored energy unchanged until it is given a suitable opportunity to return this stored energy to some load. For ex-

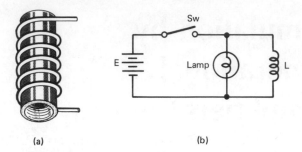

(a)   (b)

Fig. 3–1   Inductor characteristics. **(a)** Basic physical construction; **(b)** Demonstration circuit.

ample, a flywheel returns its stored energy to the brake that slows down its speed of rotation. An inductor returns its stored energy to the resistor that is switched across its terminals in place of a battery as shown in Figure 3–1(b). A brake converts ("uses up") mechanical energy in the form of heat. Similarly, a resistor converts electrical energy into heat energy.

Conversion of stored electrical energy into light and heat is demonstrated by the arrangement shown in Figure 3–1(b). A comparatively large inductor is employed, so that appreciable electrical energy can be stored. When switch Sw is closed, the lamp glows for a short time. This fact demonstrates that coil L opposes current buildup, thereby causing current to flow through the lamp. On the other hand, after the current buildup in the coil is completed, the coil no longer opposes its current flow, and the coil acts as a short-circuit across the lamp. In turn, the lamp then stops glowing. However, if switch Sw is now opened, the lamp flashes brightly for a short time. This fact demonstrates that stored electrical energy in the coil has been returned to the external circuit and converted into light and heat.

Electrical energy is stored by an inductor in the form of a magnetic field, as depicted in Figure 3–2. The strength of this field is directly proportional to the current that flows through the winding. Buildup of the magnetic field and current flow lags behind the voltage that is applied when the switch is closed. It is important to recognize that it is the buildup of the magnetic field in an inductor that opposes current flow and causes it to lag behind the applied voltage. In other words, as the magnetic field is being built up in Figure 3–2, the magnetic lines of force are expanding outward and cutting the coil turns. This cutting action *induces* a voltage in the turns which opposes the applied battery voltage. We call this opposing voltage a *counter electromotive force* (CEMF), or the voltage of self-induction. It is important to understand

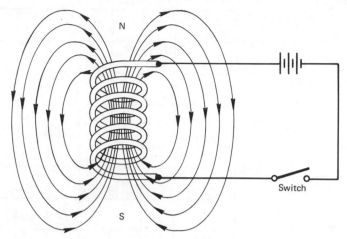

Fig. 3-2 An inductor stores energy in the form of a magnetic field.

CEMF, because it is a basic factor in the operation of simulated inductance with operational amplifiers.

When the applied voltage to an inductor is switched off, the magnetic field that has been established then starts to collapse inwards. In so doing, the magnetic lines of force cut the coil turns in the opposite direction from before. This cutting action again induces a CEMF, but with opposite polarity to the first CEMF described above. Accordingly, this CEMF tends to maintain current flow through the winding, in spite of the fact that no battery voltage is being applied to the coil. It is this CEMF that causes the lamp in Figure 3-1(b) to flash briefly when switch Sw is opened, after being closed previously. Again, this is lagging action, because the current that causes the lamp to flash is flowing after switch Sw is opened.

A small coil has a small inductance, whereas a large coil has a large inductance. Inductance is measured in Henrys. A Henry is defined as the inductance of a coil that permits the current to increase at the rate of 1 ampere per second when 1 volt is applied to the coil terminals. Figure 3-3 shows the current rise in an ideal 1-Hy coil. When 1 volt is applied to the inductor, the current increases at the rate of 1 ampere per second. The opposition that an inductor exhibits to a change in current is called inductive reactance. Reactance is measured in ohms. Note that reactance is different from resistance, not only because reactance does not convert energy, but also because the reactance of a coil does not oppose current flow—it only opposes any *change* in current flow.

The ohmic measure of reactance is shown to good advantage by consideration of an ideal inductor connected to an ac voltage source, as

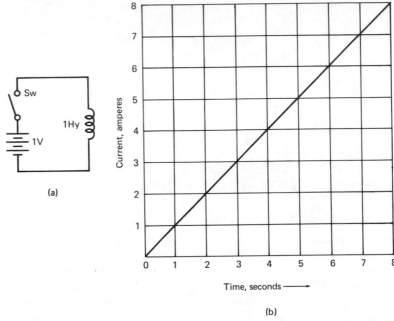

Fig. 3–3   Ideal inductor energized by a dc voltage source. **(a)** Circuit; **(b)** Current flow versus time.

depicted in Figure 3–4. If the applied voltage is doubled, the current through the inductor is doubled. Or, the reactance of the inductor is given by this voltage/current ratio:

$$X_L = \frac{E_{ac}}{I_{ac}} \text{ ohms} \qquad (3\text{–}1)$$

Next, if the frequency of the applied voltage is doubled, the value of the reactance is doubled. In other words, inductive reactance is proportional to frequency:

$$X_L = 2\pi f L \text{ ohms} \qquad (3\text{–}2)$$

where L is in Henrys, and f is in Hertz

Next, consider the basic characteristics of capacitance. A capacitor is a *two-terminal device* consisting essentially of a pair of spaced metal plates, as depicted in Figure 3–5. An ideal capacitor has an electrical property called capacitance, which is associated with energy storage. Electrical energy is stored by a capacitor in the form of an electrostatic field. This mode of energy storage is characterized by a current flow

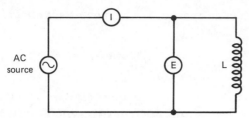

Fig. 3–4 Inductive reactance is equal to an E/I ratio.

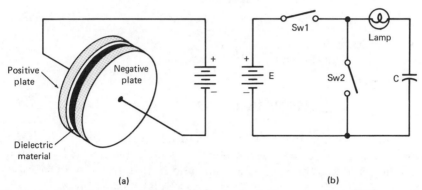

(a)   (b)

Fig. 3–5 Capacitor characteristics. **(a)** Basic physical construction; **(b)** Demonstration circuit.

that leads the applied voltage to the capacitor. As an illustration, consider the circuit action in Figure 3–5(b) when switch Sw1 is closed. There is an inrush of current from the battery into the capacitor, and this current flow causes the lamp to flash briefly. As soon as the capacitor is fully charged (comes up to full voltage) the lamp stops glowing. Thus, the current leads the voltage.

To demonstrate that the capacitor has stored electrical energy which can be returned to the external circuit, Sw1 may be opened, and Sw2 then closed. The lamp will flash briefly as the stored energy in the capacitor discharges through the lamp. Note that a capacitor opposes any *change* in voltage, whereas an inductor opposes any change in current. A small capacitor has a small capacitance, and a large capacitor has a large capacitance. Capacitance is measured in Farads. A Farad is defined as the capacitance that will store 1 coulomb when 1 volt is applied to its terminals. A coulomb is a quantity of electricity equal to 1 ampere flowing for 1 second. The opposition that a capacitor exhibits to a change in voltage is called capacitive reactance, and is measured in ohms. Capacitive reactance is different from resistance because reactance does not convert energy.

The reactance of a capacitor is given by its ac voltage/current ratio:

$$X_C = \frac{E_{ac}}{I_{ac}} \text{ ohms} \qquad (3\text{-}3)$$

Next if the frequency of the applied ac voltage is doubled, the value of the reactance is halved. In other words, capacitive reactance is inversely proportional to frequency:

$$X_C = \frac{1}{2\pi f C} \text{ ohms} \qquad (3\text{-}4)$$

where C is in Farads, and f is in Hertz

3.2 PHASE RELATIONS IN LC CIRCUITS

Phase relations are of basic importance in simulation of inductance by RC op-amp circuitry. Figure 3–6 shows how the sine-wave current in an inductor lags the applied voltage and how the current in a capacitor leads the applied voltage. These phase relations are always present in an ac circuit, as exemplified in Figure 3–7. Note that the voltage across the inductor is 180° out of phase with the voltage across the capacitor. Power is alternately stored by the capacitor, and then by the inductor. A series LCR circuit is essentially a bandpass filter, because the maximum current flow in the circuit occurs at its resonant frequency:

$$f_o = \frac{1}{2\pi\sqrt{LC}} \text{ Hertz} \qquad (3\text{-}5)$$

where f_o is the resonant frequency,

L is in Henrys

C is in Farads

3.3 SIMULATION OF L BY C IN FILTERS

There are various ways in which inductance can be simulated by capacitance in filter circuits. Simulation is uncomplicated in elementary filters, such as shown in Figure 3–8. An RC circuit is equivalent to an RL circuit with respect to frequency characteristics if the inductance in

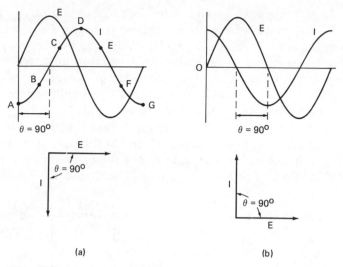

(a) (b)

Fig. 3–6 Phase relations for ideal inductance and capacitance. **(a)** Voltage-current relation for inductor; **(b)** Voltage-current relation for capacitor.

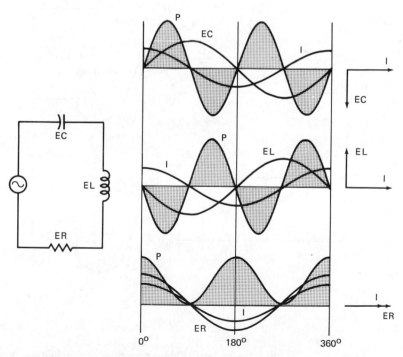

Fig. 3–7 Voltage, current, and power relations in R, C, and L.

Henrys is equal to R^2C, as shown in Figure 3–8(a) and (b). In other words, the two circuits have the same time constant. This equality follows from the relation $RC = L/R$, a relation that can be shown by mathematical analysis of the two circuits. As a practical note, when a comparatively large inductor is used, the output waveform may differ considerably from the waveform predicted by simple theory, because a large inductor has substantial distributed capacitance.

Note that the equivalent circuits in Figure 3–8(a) and (b) become high-pass filters, or differentiating circuits, if the output is taken from across the inductor in (a), and from across the resistor in (b). As a numerical example of equivalency, if L1 = 1 mH, and R1 = 1,000 ohms,

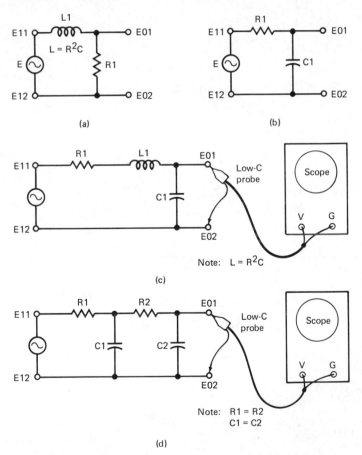

Fig. 3–8 Inductance simulation by capacitance in elementary filters. **(a)** An RL low-pass filter, or integrating circuit; **(b)** Equivalent RC low-pass filter, or integrating circuit; **(c)** A series RLC low-pass filter, or integrating circuit; **(d)** Equivalent two-section RC low-pass filter, or integrating circuit.

then C1 = 0.001 μF. Next, observe the simulation of inductance by RC circuitry in Figure 3–8(c) and (d). In this case, a series LCR low-pass filter, or integrating circuit, has an equivalent circuit consisting of a two-section RC low-pass filter, or integrating circuit. The foregoing examples of simulation are instructive. However, it should not be supposed that any inductive filter can be simulated by uncomplicated RC circuitry. To the contrary, most inductive filter configurations can be simulated by RC circuitry only if op amps are included.

It will be recognized that the equivalency in Figure 3–8(a) and (b) does not extend beyond the fact that both circuits have the same output waveform. Note that the input impedance in Figure 3–8(a) is inductive (a lagging current is drawn), whereas the input impedance in Figure 3–8(b) is capacitive (a leading current is drawn). In other words, this is not strictly an example of inductance simulation. Instead, it is an example of simulation of an input-output waveform characteristic. The same observation applies to the equivalency in Figure 3–8(c) and (d). Further, it should be noted that the input impedance in Figure 3–8(a) increases as the operating frequency increases, whereas the input impedance in Figure 3–8(b) decreases as the operating frequency increases. Similarly, the output impedances of the two circuits vary differently with frequency.

3.4 PHASE RELATIONS IN TWO-TERMINAL AND FOUR-TERMINAL CIRCUITS

Figure 3–9(a) shows an example of a two-terminal LCR series circuit; it has the frequency and phase characteristics depicted in Figure 3–9(b). This phase characteristic represents the lead or lag of the circuit current with respect to the applied voltage as the operating frequency varies from a low value to a high value. Note that the circuit draws a leading current at low frequencies, and draws a lagging current at high frequencies. In other words, the input impedance is capacitive at low frequencies, and is inductive at high frequencies. At the resonant frequency f_o, the input impedance is resistive (phase angle is 0°). At the limits of the circuit's frequency response, the phase angle is 90° leading, or 90° lagging.

Next, Figure 3–10 shows an example of a two-terminal LCR parallel circuit; it has the frequency and phase characteristics depicted in Figure 3–10(b). Note that the circuit draws a lagging current at low frequencies, and draws a leading current at high frequencies. In other words, the input impedance is inductive at low frequencies, and is capacitive at high frequencies. At the resonant frequency f_o, the input

put voltage will be reversed in polarity, or shifted in phase by 180°. As shown in Figure 3–11(b), the I + 180° sine wave is effectively in an inductive relation to E, inasmuch as it lags E by 90°. In other words, the necessary electrical relations are available to devise an RC op-amp network that will "look" inductive to an ac input voltage.

A network for inductance simulation necessarily employs feedback in such a manner that the current which is drawn in response to an applied ac voltage is dominated by the output current of the op amp. One basic form is called a *gyrator*, and its circuit action is given in reference to Figure 3–12 by the equations:

$$V_1 = AI_2 \tag{3–6}$$

$$I_1 = -BV_2 \tag{3–7}$$

where A and B are constants.

$$Z_{in} = \frac{V_1}{I_1} = \frac{-AI_1}{BV_2} = \frac{A}{BX_C} \tag{3–8}$$

$$Z_{in} = \frac{A}{B} \cdot \frac{1}{1/j\omega\,C} = j\omega\,\frac{CA}{B} \tag{3–9}$$

This result denotes a simulated inductance with a value of CA/B Henrys. A positive $j\omega$ term appears in the final term because the network is defined to draw a current in accordance with equation (3–7).

An example of inductance simulation by op-amp circuitry is shown in Figure 3–13. Here, an LCR high-pass filter has been converted into op-amp RC form. In other words, the inductor in the LCR filter has been replaced by op-amp circuitry. A high-pass filter, as explained previously, rejects or attenuates low frequencies but passes high frequencies from the input to the output of the filter. Note that the op amp employs positive feedback in this application. The circuit action in Figure 3–13(a) can be summarized as follows:

1. Capacitor C develops increasing reactance at lower frequencies and thereby opposes the passage of low frequencies.
2. Inductor L develops decreasing reactance at lower frequencies and tends to shunt low frequencies to ground, thereby further attenuating the low-frequency output.
3. Capacitor C develops decreasing reactance at higher frequencies and thereby permits passage of high frequencies.
4. Inductor L develops increasing reactance at higher frequencies and thereby permits passage of high frequencies, instead of shunting them to ground.

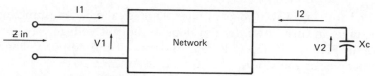

Fig. 3–12   Gyrator block diagram.

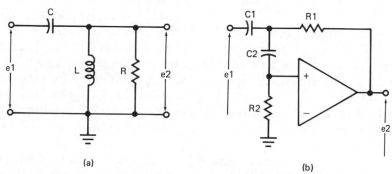

(a)   (b)

Fig. 3–13   Inductance simulation in a high-pass filter. **(a)** Conventional LCR filter circuit; **(b)** Inductor simulated by op-amp circuitry.

Next, an equivalent circuit action is provided by the configuration of Figure 3–13(b) as follows:

1. Capacitor C1 develops increasing reactance at lower frequencies and thereby opposes the passage of low frequencies.

2. Capacitor C2 develops increasing reactance at lower frequencies which in turn reduces the input signal voltage into the op amp.

3. Capacitors C1 and C2 develop decreasing reactance at higher frequencies and thereby permit passage of high frequencies.

4. Capacitor C2 applies increasing input signal voltage into the op amp at higher frequencies, and the output signal voltage is increased by the gain of the op amp at high frequencies.

Note that the amount of positive feedback utilized in the configuration of Figure 3–13(b) must not be so great that the op amp breaks into oscillation. The output voltage at high frequencies increases as the input signal voltage is increased, up to the point that the transistors in the op amp are overdriven. Beyond this input level, the output waveform will become limited or clipped.

Passive filters such as depicted in Figure 3–13(a) have a characteristic transient response, in addition to their steady-state response. Similarly, active filters such as depicted in Figure 3–13(b) have both steady-state and transient responses. The frequency response of a filter characterizes its steady-state response. On the other hand, the response of a filter to a suddenly applied DC input voltage characterizes its transient response. Figure 3–14 shows how a battery voltage can be suddenly switched into an LCR high-pass filter. This is called a step-function input voltage. In turn, the filter develops an output voltage waveform as shown in Figure 3–14(b). The rate of decay of the output voltage becomes slower as the values of L, C, and R are increased.

Active filters such as the op-amp RC high-pass filter depicted in Figure 3–13(b) have a similar transient response. With reference to Figure 3–15(a), consider the circuit action when switch Sw is closed. First, the step function of voltage seen in Figure 3–15(b) is applied to C1. In turn, a surge of voltage immediately appears across R2 from C2, and a differentiated pulse is applied to the input of the op amp. This pulse is amplified with the result that e_2 immediately rises to its maximum value. At the same time, positive feedback voltage is applied to C1-C2 via R1. This feedback modifies the response of the RC circuitry as depicted in Figure 3–16. In other words, the circuit action can be summarized as follows:

1. A two-section differentiating circuit is provided by C1R1 and C2R2. By itself, this two-section differentiator produces a voltage waveform across R2 in accordance with the "resistive transient component" indicated in Figure 3–16.

2. Positive feedback from the op-amp output to C1-C2 introduces simulated inductive action, with the result that an "inductive transient component" is included in the total response, as indicated in Figure 3–16.

3. Combination of the two transient components results in the output voltage waveform e_2, which is essentially the same as the voltage output waveform depicted in Figure 3–14.

3.6   OTA GYRATOR ARRANGEMENTS

A useful network for inductance simulation employs an operational transconductance amplifier (OTA) in a gyrator configuration. An OTA has a comparatively high output resistance, which provides added utility in gyrator application. The forward transfer characteristic of an OTA is defined as the relation of output current to input voltage. By way of comparison, the forward transfer characteristic of an operational voltage amplifier (OVA) such as discussed previously, is defined as the relation of output voltage to input voltage. Although the gain of an OTA could be expressed as an output/input voltage ratio, its high output resistance complicates the equations, and the OTA forward characteristic is best described by a transconductance term. Note that an ideal OVA would have zero output resistance, whereas an ideal OTA would have infinite output resistance.

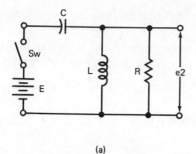
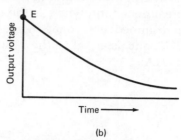

(a)

(b)

Fig. 3–14 Transient response of an LCR high-pass filter. **(a)** Arrangement for apply-ing a step function of voltage; **(b)** Response of filter to a step-function input.

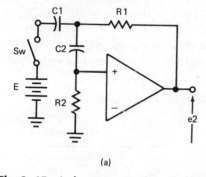
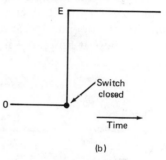

(a)

(b)

Fig. 3–15 Inductance simulator for functional analysis. **(a)** Source voltage provided by battery and switch; **(b)** Step function of voltage is applied when Sw is closed.

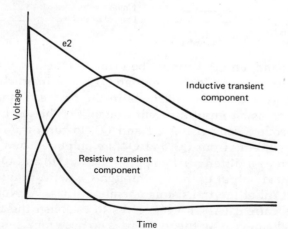

Fig. 3–16 Basic transient components of output from inductance simulator con-figuration.

The output circuit of an OTA is regarded as an infinite-impedance current generator, whereas the output circuit of an OVA is regarded as a zero-impedance voltage generator. Transconductance is symbolized by G_m, and is equal to the ratio of output current to input voltage for the OTA:

$$G_m = \frac{i_{out}}{e_{in}} \text{ mhos} \qquad (3\text{--}10)$$

where i_{out} is in ampere units

e_{in} is in volt units

An OTA has a high input resistance, as does an OVA. Table 3–1 summarizes comparative characteristics of ideal OTA and OVA devices. If an OTA is operated into a suitable resistive load, with a negative-feedback loop, it functions in essentially the same manner as an OVA.

TABLE 3–1

Comparative Characteristics of Ideal OTA and OVA Devices

	OTA		OVA
Input impedance	_____	High	_____
Input bias current	_____	Low	_____
Offset	_____	0	_____
Gain	High Transconductance		High Voltage gain
Bandwidth	_____	Infinite	_____
Slew rate	_____	Infinite	_____
Output voltage	_____	Limited by supplies	_____
Output current	_____	Limited by supplies	_____
Output impedance	Infinite		0
Operating current	Adjustable		Adjustable

On the other hand, an OVA cannot be made to function like an OTA. Figure 3–17 shows the basic circuit for an OTA. It is instructive to consider the voltage and current relations in the device. Transistors Q3 and Q4 function as an input differential amplifier, biased by the constant-current source comprising Q1 and Q2. In turn, the differential output-signal currents from Q3 and Q4 are amplified by Q7 and Q8 which function as a differential amplifier. Next, Q10 and Q11 convert the double-ended output of the Q5-through-Q9 network into a single-ended output. All of the transistors operate in Class A. Note that the amplifier bias current (ABC) level serves to establish the bias on all transistors in the device. In theory there is no need for a signal ground because the input signal is differential and the output is a current source.

Details of OTA operation and discussion of elaborated OTA con-

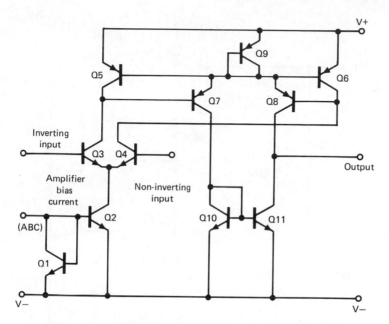

Fig. 3–17 Basic OTA configuration.

figurations are resumed subsequently. At this time, consider the basic OTA gyrator arrangement depicted in Figure 3–18. An OTA is particularly suitable for gyrator application because of its high output impedance. To anticipate subsequent discussion, it will be shown that an OVA gyrator is suitable for application in circuits with one end of the simulated inductance grounded. On the other hand, an OTA gyrator can be applied in circuits that employ a floating simulated inductance (both ends of the simulated inductance operating above ground potential). For practical application, note that simulated inductance values of approximately 10,000 Henrys can be obtained in a configuration comprising a pair of OTA's.

With reference to Figure 3–18, a gyrator arrangement is shown which provides this very high value of simulated inductance with the use of an external 3-μF capacitor. As noted above, there is no ground reference in this type of circuit, and the simulated inductance may operate as a floating inductor in an audio filter, or other signal-processing network. In effect, the simulated inductance is isolated from the power supplies by the high input and output impedances of the C A's. An attenuation network is provided around the input of both op amps for extension of the differential operating range of each OTA approximately 100 times. This attenuation network reduces the transconductance value 100 times and thereby further increases the gyration resistance. Provi-

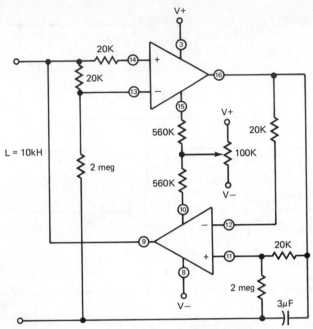

Fig. 3–18 A gyrator arrangement utilizing two op amps.

sion for adjustable bias current is made so that OTA transconductance can be directly controlled, thereby varying the gyration resistance inversely. In turn, the value of the simulated inductance is varied.

Note that a two-terminal network such as the gyrator depicted in Figure 3–18 is sometimes called a *single-port network*. Again, a (basically) four-terminal network as in Figures 3–14 and 3–15 is called a *two-port network*. Since there are two pairs of input terminals and one pair of output terminals provided in Figure 3–17, this arrangement is called a *three-port device*. A gyrator arrangement using two OVA's is depicted in Figure 3–19. From the viewpoint of application, it is a one-port network. However, from the viewpoint of the circuit designer it is regarded as a two-port network with capacitance connected across one port, and resistance connected across the other port. The value of inductance simulated by the gyrator in Figure 3–19 is given by the equation:

$$L = \frac{R1 \times R2 \times R4 \times C1}{R3} \text{ Hy} \tag{3–11}$$

Observe that when a gyrator is designed with OVA's, as in Figure 3–19, one of the terminals must be connected to ground. This is in contrast to the gyrator designed with OTA's in Figure 3–18, wherein

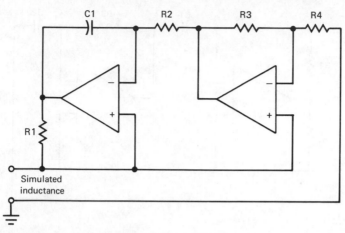

Fig. 3–19 A gyrator arrangement using two OVA's.

both terminals may operate above ground potential. Therefore, an OVA gyrator finds application chiefly in high-pass active filters, whereas an OTA gyrator may be employed in either low-pass or high-pass active filters.

3.7 FREQUENCY-DEPENDENT NEGATIVE-RESISTANCE CIRCUITS

Another method of reactance simulation utilizes frequency-dependent negative-resistance (FDNR) circuits instead of a gyrator configuration. Figure 3–20 shows a typical FDNR circuit. It is frequency-dependent because the reactances of C1 and C2 vary with frequency. Because it is frequency-dependent, it serves as a filter. Unlike a gyrator, an FDNR circuit draws a leading current when an ac voltage is applied to its terminals. The FDNR circuit exemplified in Figure 3–20 employs OVA's, and one of its terminals is necessarily grounded. *Negative resistance* is a characteristic of a device or network that draws less current when more voltage is applied. All circuits that utilize positive feedback exhibit negative resistance over their useful operating range. An FDNR finds its chief application in low-pass filter circuits that require very large values of simulated capacitance. The capacitance value simulated by the FDNR circuit in Figure 3–20 is given by the equation:

$$C = \frac{R1 \times R3 \times C1 \times C2}{R2} \text{ farads} \qquad (3\text{--}12)$$

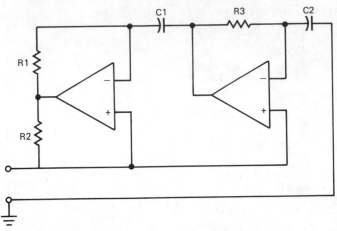

Fig. 3–20 An FDNR circuit for simulating a large capacitance.

3.8 BASIC OPERATIONAL AMPLIFIER TEST PROCEDURES

Operational amplifiers can be checked and their basic characteristics measured with comparatively simple test arrangements. For example, the circuit shown in Figure 3–21(a), when used with suitable instruments, permits precise measurements of dc open-loop gain, open-loop gain stability versus temperature, open-loop gain versus supply-voltage variation, open-loop input impedance, and open-loop output impedance. Gain is measured by an ac method which eliminates problems from dc offset and drift. A frequency of 10 Hz is employed. Note that the 1000-μF capacitor has a reactance of approximately 16 ohms at 10 Hz. In turn, the ideal voltage-gain figure is approximately 63,000 times, or 96 dB, in accordance with the equation:

$$\frac{E_0}{E_1} = \frac{R_0 + X_C}{X_C} \qquad (3-13)$$

In practice, a measured gain figure of 80 dB would be considered satisfactory or normal. On the other hand, a gain of 60 dB for example, would indicate that the op amp is defective, and should be rejected.

OPEN-LOOP DC VOLTAGE GAIN: Measurement of the open-loop dc-voltage gain of the op amp is made with a sine-wave test signal supplied by an audio oscillator operating at 10 Hz and an output level of 100 μv. In turn, the output is measured with a TVM or oscilloscope. An oscillo-

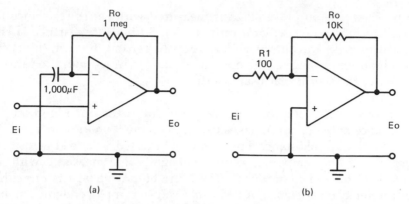

Fig. 3–21 Op amp test circuits. **(a)** For measurement of ac open-loop characteristics; **(b)** A X100 amplifier circuit for maximum-output and bandwidth tests.

scope is preferable because it will show whether the output waveform is being clipped or otherwise distorted. Waveform distortion is associated with incorrect gain calculations.

OPEN-LOOP GAIN STABILITY VERSUS TEMPERATURE: The foregoing test arrangement is also employed to measure the open-loop gain stability of the op amp versus temperature. A dB gain measurement is first made with the op amp at 0°C, and then with the op amp at 50°C. In turn, the gain stability is defined by the expression:

$$\text{Stability} = \frac{dB_1 - dB_2}{50°C} \tag{3–14}$$

OPEN-LOOP GAIN STABILITY VERSUS SUPPLY VOLTAGE: The foregoing test arrangement is also utilized to measure the open-loop gain stability of the op amp versus supply-voltage variation. A dB gain measurement is first made with the supply voltage at 10 percent above bogie value, and then with the supply voltage at 10 percent below bogie value. In turn, the gain stability is defined by the expression:

$$\text{Stability} = \frac{dB_1 - dB_2}{20\%} \tag{3–15}$$

OPEN-LOOP INPUT IMPEDANCE: Measurement of the open-loop input impedance of the op amp utilizes the foregoing test arrangement with the addition of a decade resistance box. The output voltage is first measured with the audio-oscillator signal applied directly to the op amp. Then, the output voltage is measured with series resistance inserted in the audio-oscillator output lead. Sufficient resistance is employed to make the output voltage drop 10 percent. In turn, the open-loop input impedance of the op amp is equal to nine times the value of the series resistance that was inserted.

OPEN-LOOP OUTPUT IMPEDANCE: Measurement of the open-loop output impedance of the op amp makes use of the same items as above, except that the decade resistance box is now connected as a load across the output of the op amp. The output voltage is first measured with infinite load resistance (no load). Then, the output voltage is measured with finite load resistance. A resistance value is employed which makes the output voltage drop 10 percent. In turn, the open-loop output impedance of the op amp is equal to 1/9 of the load-resistance value. Note that the output waveform must not be clipped, or the calculation will be in error; reduce the input signal voltage, if necessary.

MAXIMUM OUTPUT CAPABILITY: Measurement of the maximum output voltage and current capability of an op amp utilizes the circuit depicted in Figure 3–21(b), and the same test equipment as above. The decade resistance box is connected across the output of the op amp, and is set to the desired value of load resistance. Starting from the initial 100 μv level, the input signal amplitude is increased until distortion becomes perceptible in the output waveform. The signal amplitude is then backed off slightly. Maximum output-voltage capability is then measured on the oscilloscope screen. In turn, the maximum output-current capability is calculated, observing that R_o and R_L operate in parallel. The current value is given by the equation:

$$I_{out} = \frac{V_{out}}{R_L \parallel R_o} \tag{3–16}$$

OPEN-LOOP BANDWIDTH: Measurement of the open-loop bandwidth of an op amp employs the circuit shown in Figure 3–21(b), with an audio oscillator and a TVM or oscilloscope. The audio oscillator is set for a signal level of 30 mV into the op amp. Then, the operating frequency is increased from the initial value of 10 Hz to a value that causes the output signal level to decrease to a level of 30 mV. This is called the small-signal open-loop bandwidth of the op amp. On the other hand, the full-power response is defined differently, and is often the dominant design factor. The full-power response of an op amp is measured with sufficient drive from the audio oscillator to develop maximum rated output voltage at 10 Hz. Then, the operating frequency is increased until the maximum rated output voltage starts to decrease. This is called the full-power response frequency of the op amp.

As noted previously, the circuit depicted in Figure 3–21(b) is also used to check other characteristics of an op amp. These further test procedures are explained in greater detail subsequently.

REVIEW QUESTIONS

1. Explain CEMF as the term applies to an inductor.
2. What is the relationship between the current and voltage in an inductor?
3. What is the relationship between the current and voltage in a capacitor?
4. What is a gyrator?
5. What limits the amount of feedback allowed in a circuit, such as shown in Fig. 3–13(b)?
6. What values of inductance can we simulate with a circuit comprised of a pair of OTA's?
7. What is a three-port circuit?
8. Where does a OVA gyrator find most application?
9. Where does a OTA gyrator find most application?
10. What is the characteristic of a negative resistance network?
11. What is the simulated capacitance value of the circuit in Fig. 3–20 when $R_1 = 100k$ ohm, $R_3 = 200k$ ohm, $C_1 = .01\mu F$, and $C_2 = .1\mu F$?
12. List seven basic operational amplifier measurements.

4 · Op-Amp Instrumentation Applications

4.1 GENERAL CONSIDERATIONS

Operational amplifiers are used in various instrumentation applications. As an illustration, op amps are employed in active oscilloscope probes such as differentiating, integrating, and logarithmic probes. Op amps are utilized in strain gages, thermocouple bridges, high-gain active filters, buffers, and sample-and-hold amplifiers. Other applications include precision voltage references, paired operation in true instrumentation amplifiers, replacement of chopper-type amplifiers, and comparators in various instruments such as digital voltmeters. They are also used as oscillators; for example, op amps may be key components in triggered-sweep circuits (triggered time bases) for oscilloscopes. Instrumentation applications employ op amps in both linear and nonlinear modes.

4.2 DIGITAL VOLTMETER ARRANGEMENTS

A digital voltmeter (DVM) such as illustrated in Figure 4–1 indicates a measured voltage value in the form of numerals, instead of a pointer indication on a scale, as in the case of an analog voltmeter. Since the applied voltage may have any value within the range of the voltmeter, the input to the instrument is of analog form. In turn, the numerical display is of digital form. Therefore, an analog-to-digital converter (A-to-D converter) is required in the instrument. Seven basic types of A-to-D conversion are employed in various designs of digital voltmeters. These basic designs are termed (1) ramp, (2) staircase ramp, (3) dual ramp integrating, (4) integrating, (5) integrating and potentiometric, (6) successive approximation, and (7) continuous balance.

As an illustration, a voltage value can be converted into a proportional time interval, during which an accurate oscillator (clock) is started and then stopped. In turn, the number of pulses produced by the os-

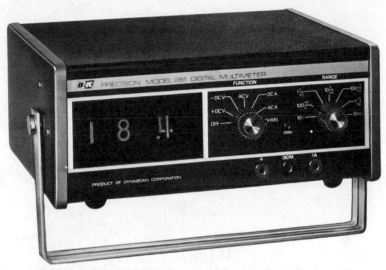

Fig. 4–1 A digital voltmeter. (*Courtesy, B & K Mfg. Co.*)

cillator actuate an electronic counter that has a digital readout in terms
of volts. Basically, a ramp-type digital voltmeter measures the time that
a linear ramp (sawtooth waveform) takes to fall from the input voltage
level to ground potential, or, the time that it takes to rise from ground
potential to the input voltage level. This time interval is measured by a
digital counter energized by clock pulses, and displayed on in-line indicating tubes in numerical form. Thus, although the input to the
instrument is of continuous (analog) form, the measured value is displayed in discrete (digital) form. Figure 4–2 depicts the principle of
voltage-to-time conversion. At the start of the measurement operation,
a ramp generator is triggered and a linear decrease occurs in the ramp
voltage. Soon the ramp voltage reaches the same value as the voltage
being measured, and this first coincidence triggers a count gate,
whereby clock pulses are applied to the digital counter. The count gate
remains open until the ramp reaches ground potential (zero volts),
whereupon the count gate is closed, and the voltage value is indicated
numerically.

Note that the time interval over which the count gate is open is
proportional to the input voltage value. Therefore, the number of clock
pulses that pass into the electronic counter is also proportional to the
input voltage value. Figure 4–3 shows a block diagram for a ramp-type
digital voltmeter. The basic cycle sequence consists of sampling, display, and reset sequences. When an input voltage is applied to the
ranging and attenuator section, a reference voltage is applied to one
input terminal of the input-comparator op amp, and the ramp generator

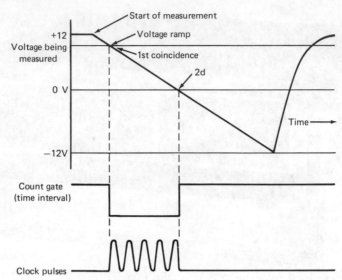

Fig. 4–2   Principle of voltage-to-time conversion.

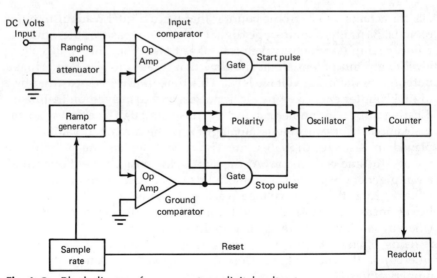

Fig. 4–3   Block diagram for a ramp-type digital voltmeter.

is started. In turn, the output from the ramp generator is applied to the other input terminal of the input-comparator op amp. A short time later (Figure 4–2), the ramp voltage becomes equal to the reference voltage. In turn, the output from the input-comparator op amp suddenly changes in polarity and triggers the start-pulse gate.

Next, the output from the start-pulse gate switches the oscillator on, and clock pulses are applied to the electronic counter. In turn, the oscillator continues operating until the ramp voltage reaches ground potential. That is, the ground-comparator op amp is referenced to ground potential. In turn, when the ramp voltage passes through zero (ground potential), the output from the ground-comparator op amp suddenly changes in polarity and triggers the stop-pulse gate. Thereupon, the oscillator is switched off and the electronic counter stops. Thus, the readout section indicates numerically the value of the reference voltage that was applied to the input-comparator op amp. Also, the reset circuitry is actuated so that the foregoing sequence of circuit actions can be repeated. As explained in greater detail below, a sample-rate section is included in the instrument to enable the DVM to "follow" a varying input voltage.

All DVM's have a basic cycle sequence of sampling, display, and reset operations. With reference to Figure 4–3, a units counter is first actuated. After the ninth count, a carry pulse is fed to the tens counter. After the 99th count, a carry pulse is fed to the hundreds counter. After the 999th count, a carry pulse is fed to a warning lamp which indicates to the operator that the range switch is set too low. The sample-rate function depicted in Figure 4–3 permits the readout value to decrease in case the voltage under measurement starts to decrease. This sample-rate section is controlled by a relaxation oscillator (pulse generator) that triggers and resets the counters to zero every half second. In turn, the display circuits store each reading until a new sample value occurs, whereupon the counters are actuated and the former readout value is replaced by the new value. Display-circuit storage eliminates "blinking" that would otherwise occur at the sampling rate. After the operator completes the measurement, the readout automatically returns to zero.

Next, Figure 4–4 shows a block diagram for the staircase ramp type of DVM. Voltage measurements are made on the basis of comparing the input voltage to that of an internally generated staircase ramp voltage. When the staircase ramp voltage becomes equal to the input voltage, the op-amp comparator suddenly reverses its output polarity and stops the ramp. In turn, the readout unit displays the number of steps that made the staircase ramp voltage equal to the input voltage. The sampling rate in this example is 2 Hz. At the end of a sample, a reset pulse returns the staircase voltage to zero. "Blinking" is eliminated by temporary storage, as explained previously. Each decade counter unit is connected to a digital-to-analog converter (D-to-A converter). Outputs from these converters build up the comparison (staircase) voltage. Note that the comparator op amp functions in the nonlinear mode, whereas the input amplifier, reset amplifier, and staircase amplifier function in the linear mode.

It is instructive to consider the operation of the integrating type of DVM. A block diagram of the voltage-to-frequency converter section is shown in Figure 4–5. This design of DVM indicates the average value

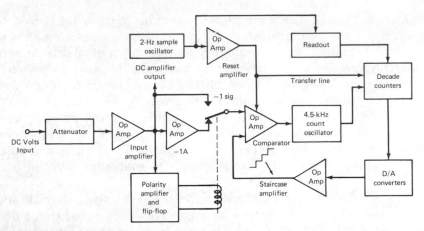

Fig. 4–4 Block diagram of a staircase-ramp type of DVM.

of a varying input voltage over a certain time interval, whereas a ramp-type DVM "follows" a varying input voltage. In the example of Figure 4–5, integration is employed with a voltage-to-frequency converter. Essentially, the network functions as a feedback control system which controls the rate of pulse generation. In turn, the average value of the pulse train is equal to the dc input voltage value. Decade counters and a readout unit (not shown) are utilized to display the measured value. A major advantage of this form of A-to-D conversion is its ability to measure a dc-voltage value accurately in the presence of large noise pulses. In other words, the noise voltages tend to average out (cancel) over the measuring interval.

At this point, it is instructive to note that the basic op-amp integrator arrangement is often unsatisfactory in practice. Part of the input offset current tends to charge the feedback capacitor and produces a constantly changing output when no input voltage is applied. Therefore, the basic circuit must be somewhat elaborated to minimize the effect of input offset current. A current-balancing arrangement for this purpose is depicted in Figure 4–6. R2 has a value that is large compared with the reactance of C over the range of frequencies to be integrated. Note that the offset current through R2 is minimized by suitable adjustment of RP1. With respect to dc, the gain of the circuit is limited to −R2/R1; this characteristic prevents the output from gradually drifting into saturation. In case R2 is not included, eventual drift into saturation can be anticipated.

Next, a block diagram for an integrating DVM is shown in Figure 4–7. A 60-Hz clock is employed in this example, and the average value of the input voltage is measured over a 1/60-sec. sample interval. The arrangement consists basically of a voltage-to-frequency converter and

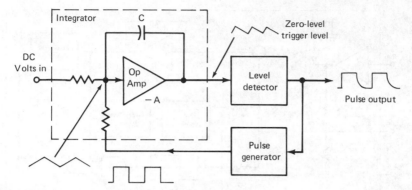

Fig. 4–5 Block diagram of a voltage-to-frequency converter for an integrating type of DVM.

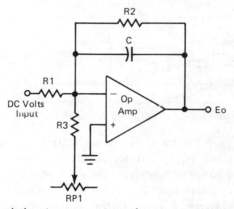

Fig. 4–6 A current-balancing arrangement for an op-amp integrator.

a counter. As explained above, a dc voltage applied to the integrator is translated into a pulse rate proportional to the value of the applied voltage. During the 1/60-sec. sample interval, the output from the converter is applied to the 10^2 decade. After the sampling period an interpolation process is utilized and pulses are fed into the 10^0 decade. Note that these pulses are proportional in value to the charge remaining on the integrating capacitor after the 1/60-sec. sampling interval. Following the interpolation process, the counts present in all of the decades are displayed on in-line digital readout tubes.

Another DVM design which provides very high accuracy is shown in the block diagram of Figure 4–8. This is called the integrating/potentiometric type of DVM. It employs an integrating-type voltmeter which measures the average value of a varying input voltage over the sampling interval, supplemented by potentiometric action which operates from precision resistance ratios and a precise reference voltage. Level com-

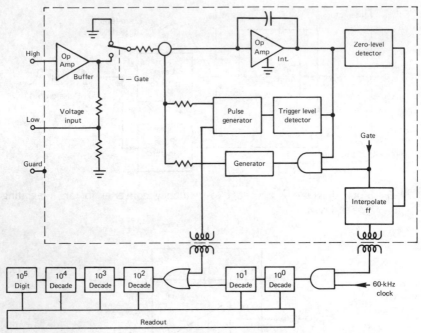

Fig. 4–7   Block diagram for an integrating-type DVM.

parisons are made on the basis of null techniques similar to those utilized in calibration of high-accuracy laboratory voltmeters. When ac-voltage values are to be measured with a DVM, an ac-dc converter is employed. A typical arrangement is shown in Figure 4–9. It is a specialized rectifier network with an output capability up to 1 volt dc. Its response is proportional to the average value of the applied ac rms volts. The incoming ac voltage is amplified and then passed through a rectifier and filter arrangement. This type of ac-dc converter can indicate correct ac voltage rms values for pure sine waveforms only.

It is instructive to consider the half-wave and full-wave precision-rectifier configurations shown in Figure 4–10. Semiconductor diodes are somewhat nonlinear, particularly at low input-signal levels. Moreover, a germanium diode does not conduct substantially until the applied voltage exceeds 0.3 volt. Similarly, a silicon diode does not conduct substantially until the applied voltage exceeds 0.7 volt. However, if instead of utilizing the diodes directly, they are operated in the feedback loop of an op amp, precise rectification can be obtained down to very small input levels. Typical configurations are shown in Figure 4–10. Either germanium or silicon diodes may be utilized.

With reference to Figure 4–10(a), note that the dc output voltage is not taken from the output terminal of the op amp, but between D2

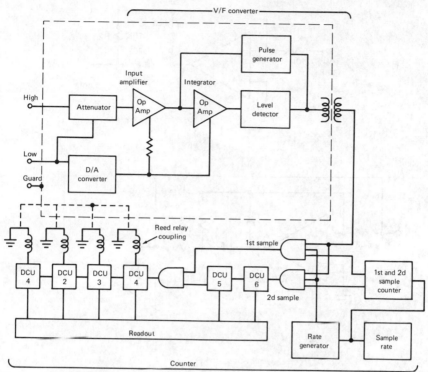

Fig. 4–8 Block diagram for an integrating/potentiometric DVM.

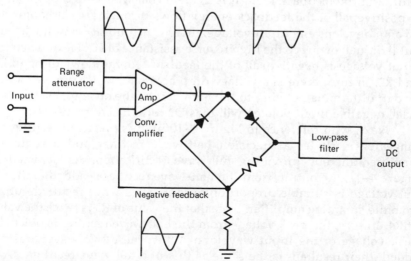

Fig. 4–9 An ac-dc converter configuration for a DVM.

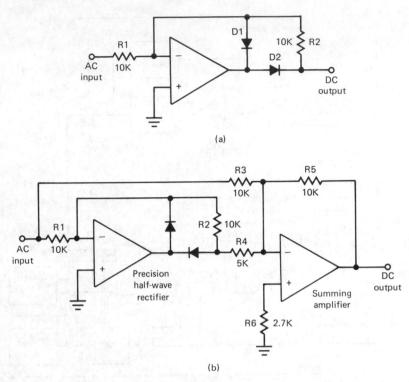

(a)

(b)

Fig. 4–10 Op-amp precision-rectifier configurations. **(a)** Half wave; **(b)** Full wave.

and R2 in the feedback loop. It is evident that when the input voltage is positive, all of the feedback energy flows through D1. Although the op amp develops an output voltage, there is no output from the dc output terminal, owing to the high reverse resistance of D2. Next, when the input voltage is negative, all of the feedback energy flows through D2 and R2. In turn, there is a voltage drcp across R2 which appears at the dc output terminal. Owing to the high gain of the op amp, even a very small negative input voltage will bias D2 for efficient rectification.

Next, with reference to Figure 4–10(b), this precision rectifier arrangement includes a precision half-wave rectifier and a summing amplifier, thereby providing full-wave rectification. As depicted in Figure 4–11, the output from the half-wave rectifier is added to the input voltage in suitable proportion to form a full-wave rectified output from the summing amplifier. Note that the value of R3 is twice the value of R4. In turn, the peak voltage from the half-wave rectifier is twice the peak voltage of the input waveform. When these two waveforms are added, their resultant is the same as that of a full-wave rectifier.

Another type of DVM, called the dual-slope integration design, is

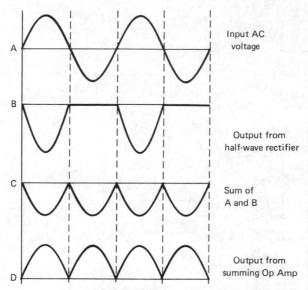

A   Input AC voltage

B   Output from half-wave rectifier

C   Sum of A and B

D   Output from summing Op Amp

Fig. 4–11 Operating waveforms in precision full-wave rectifier circuit.

shown in block form in Figure 4–12. This arrangement measures dc voltages by means of an integrator. In turn, the integrator controls a time interval which is proportional to the average value of the dc voltage to be measured. This time interval gates the counter on and off, so that the number of oscillator pulses that are totalized is proportional to the average value of the dc voltage to be measured. The dc input voltage is integrated, thereby producing an upward ramp. Integration occurs either for 1/10 or 1/60 of a second, the period being selectable by the operator for best response. This ramp voltage rises to a peak value at the end of the integration interval, and the peak value is stored. Then, a downward ramp is started by switching a precise reference voltage in opposite polarity to discharge the integrator. This discharge time is terminated by a zero-detect (comparator) circuit, and is proportional to the stored voltage value. During the discharge time interval, oscillator pulses are totalized and then indicated by the display unit.

There is a possibility of slow drift in the dual-slope integrating DVM. Accordingly, provisions are included for automatic zeroing. After the integration cycle is completed, the input amplifier (Figure 4–12) is automatically disconnected and adjusted for zero output before the next measurement is started. Thereby, the input amplifier is maintained in a precisely zeroed state while resting between integration cycles. Note that a dc-voltage measurement is made by applying the input voltage to the X input terminal. In case it is desired to measure the ratio of two dc voltages, one voltage is applied to the X input ter-

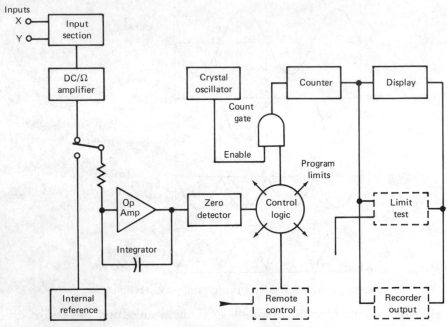

Fig. 4–12 Block diagram of a dual-slope integrating DVM.

minal and the other voltage is applied to the Y input terminal. In turn, the voltage ratio is indicated by the DVM as the X/Y value. Instrument function is the same as explained above, except that the down-slope is now determined by the Y input voltage, instead of the reference voltage.

4.3 OP-AMP TRIGGERED TIME BASE

A triggered time base that utilizes three op amps is depicted in block form in Figure 4–13, and in schematic form in Figure 4–14. This type of time base is used in lab-type oscilloscopes. Because the power output of an op amp is somewhat limited, the time base is followed by a power-transistor horizontal amplifier (not shown) to drive the cathode-ray tube. With reference to Figure 4–14, a diode limiter circuit (D1-D4) is provided to prevent overdrive of the input field-effect transistor. This FET (Q1) is included to obtain high input impedance for the incoming sync signal, thereby minimizing loading of associated circuitry. The following network comprises three op amps, one of which operates in the linear mode while the other two operate in the nonlinear mode. These op amps function as a comparator, a flip-flop, and an integrator. The integrator operates in the linear mode.

A diode limiter arrangement (D5, D6) is also placed in the input

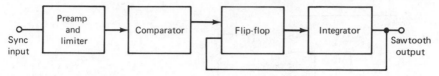

Fig. 4–13 Block diagram for an op-amp triggered time base.

circuit of the comparator, to avoid the possibility of latch-up owing to overdrive. A reference voltage level for the comparator is set by R9. When the output from the pre-amp exceeds this reference level, the output from the comparator suddenly swings from a negative voltage to a positive voltage. In turn, a positive pulse is fed into the inverting input of the flip-flop op amp. Diodes D7 and D8 ensure that negative pulses cannot enter the flip-flop. This flip-flop is basically an ac-coupled multivibrator which is overbiased so that it cannot change state unless a trigger pulse is applied. Multivibrator circuitry is explained in greater detail in the next chapter The flip-flop is in a state of positive saturation until a trigger pulse is applied to the inverting input. Then, the flip-flop changes state and goes into negative saturation. It remains in negative saturation until a trigger pulse arrives at the noninverting input. Thereupon the flip-flop changes state back into positive saturation.

When the flip-flop suddenly changes from positive saturation to negative saturation, the integrator is energized and produces a linear positive ramp (saw-tooth wave). Switch S2 provides a choice of three ramp speeds. Note that the ramp voltage is fed back to the noninverting input of the flip-flop via R15 and D10. When the ramp voltage becomes sufficiently positive, the flip-flop suddenly changes state and goes into positive saturation once again. This action also discharges the integrator capacitor suddenly, causing flyback (retrace). The time base then rests until another trigger pulse arrives at the inverting input of the flip-flop. Note that C4 is included to provide lockout (holdoff) action. In other words, if a trigger pulse happens to be applied to the inverting input of the flip-flop during the retrace interval, C4 will prevent premature initiation of a ramp.

Next, consider the operation of the integrator in Figure 4–14. A diode, D11, is connected in series with the inverting-input terminal of the op amp. In turn, the charging current of the integrating capacitor is determined by forward or reverse bias on D11. In other words, when the flip-flop is in its negatively saturated state, D11 is reverse biased and the charging current is set by R14. Thus, the sweep speed is dependent on the setting of R14, which functions as a vernier sweep-speed control. As noted previously, S2 functions as a coarse sweep-speed control. Next, when the flip-flop suddenly goes into positive saturation, D11 becomes forward-biased, and the integrating capacitor

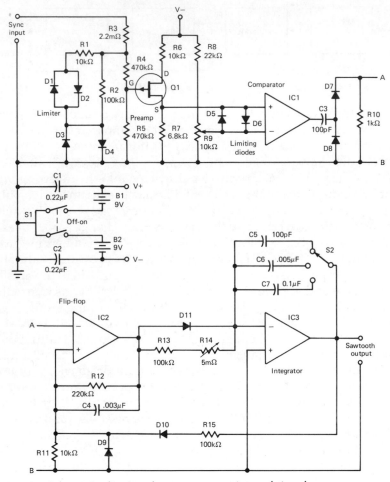

Fig. 4–14   Schematic diagram for an op-amp triggered time base.

discharges quickly through the diode. Diode D9 is included in the feedback network to ensure that negative-going voltage cannot feed back into the noninverting input of the flip-flop.

4.4   CURRENT MIRROR ACTION

Most op amps have inverting and noninverting inputs which are associated with a differential-amplifier section. On the other hand, some op amps develop a noninverting input by means of a current-differencing input stage called a current mirror. Figure 4–15 depicts the basic current-mirror configuration. Its action is essentially that of a

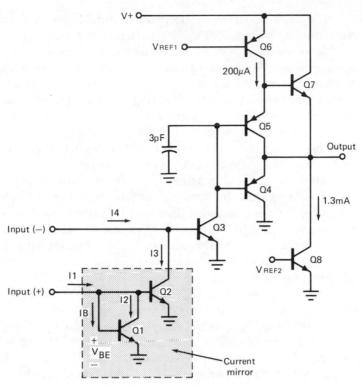

Fig. 4–15 A current-mirror op-amp configuration.

circuit which responds to a current input fed into one terminal by draw-ing an identical current input at the other terminal. Thus, when a cur-rent, I_1, is fed into the diode-connected transistor Q1, a self-bias voltage is developed across its base-emitter junction. In turn, a collector current, I_2, flows according to the equation:

$$I_2 = I_1 - 2I_B \tag{4-1}$$

This current flow produces a voltage drop across the base-emitter junction of Q1, which applies a corresponding bias to the base of Q2. Because Q1 and Q2 are matched transistors, the collector current of Q2 (I_3) is equal to I_2 and practically equal to I_1. Current I_3 must be drawn from the inverting input of the op amp; thus I_4, which is essentially equal to I_1, flows from the external circuit into the inverting input. One of the important distinctions between a conventional op amp and the current-mirror design is that the former has a very high input imped-ance, whereas the latter has a low input impedance. Therefore, the current-mirror type of op amp is called a current-operated device.

Note in Figure 4–15 that a single-polarity supply voltage is utilized by a current-mirror op amp. This is a positive power supply—a negative power supply is not required. In turn, this feature makes the current-mirror op amp easily designed into automotive electrical systems. Another attractive feature is the comparatively small number of components built into the IC package, resulting in comparatively low cost. Current-mirror op amps are designed into anti-skid, speed-control, and fuel-injection systems. Another typical application is in frequency-doubling tachometer generators, as depicted in Figure 4–16. Note the specialized symbol that is preferred to denote a current-mirror op amp. This tachometer arrangement is actuated by current pulses from the ignition system of a vehicle. In turn, the tachometer develops a dc output which is proportional to twice the input frequency. This dc output energizes a conventional milliammeter with a scale calibrated in rpm.

A symmetrical op-amp pair is utilized in the arrangement of Figure 4–16, so that there will be zero dc output when there is no input pulse train (F_{in}). Exact balance is obtained by adjustment of R3, which compensates for tolerances on op-amp characteristics. Pulses applied to C1 are differentiated, so that the positive input pulse is changed into a positive spike followed by a negative spike. Frequency doubling is an aspect of full-wave rectification, provided by diodes D1 and D2. Although D1 and D2 could be employed without an op amp, the dc output would have a comparatively low level, and a more sensitive indicating meter would be required. Therefore, it is advantageous to include the op-amp circuitry and use a lower-sensitivity (lower cost) indicating meter.

4.5 OPERATIONAL VOLTAGE-AMPLIFIER TEST PROCEDURES

As noted previously, operational amplifiers can be checked and their basic characteristics measured with comparatively simple test arrangements. It is instructive to consider how the circuit shown in Figure 4–17 is used to measure input offset voltage, input voltage drift versus temperature, input voltage drift versus supply, input voltage drift versus time, and input noise of operational voltage amplifiers.

INPUT OFFSET VOLTAGE MEASUREMENT: A standard test circuit is depicted in Figure 4–17, which is basically a X100 amplifier used for measurement of very small voltage drift and offset values. These voltages are measured at the output terminals, and are referred to the input by di-

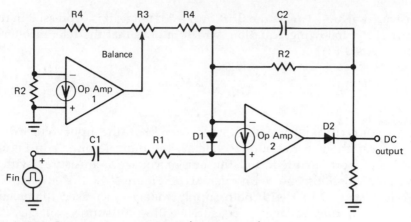

Fig. 4–16 Current-mirror op-amp tachometer configuration.

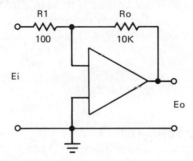

Fig. 4–17 Standard test circuit.

viding the measured value by 100. Note that in calculating load values, R_o presents a load to the output of the op amp, and must be included in the load calculations. To measure the input offset voltage, the input terminals in Figure 4–17 are short-circuited, and the voltage across the output terminals is measured with a TVM or a dc oscilloscope. This is the output offset voltage which is divided by the voltage gain of the amplifier to obtain the input offset voltage:

$$V_{in} \text{ off} = \frac{V_{out}}{100} \tag{4–2}$$

INPUT VOLTAGE DRIFT VERSUS TEMPERATURE: To measure the input voltage drift versus temperature, the test circuit shown in Figure 4–17 is employed. Two measurements of input offset voltage are made, as explained above. One measurement is made at 0°C and the other is made at 50°C. In turn, the drift is calculated as the difference between the two measured values. This is the drift over a 50° range; it is expressed in the form of the following equation, which implies that the reference temperature is 0°C:

$$\text{Drift} = \frac{\Delta V_{offset}}{50°C} \tag{4-3}$$

INPUT VOLTAGE DRIFT VERSUS SUPPLY: To measure the input voltage drift versus variation in the supply voltage, the input terminals in Figure 4–17 are short-circuited, and the output voltage is measured with a TVM or dc oscilloscope. With reference to Figure 4–18, the output voltage is measured first with both supply voltages increased 10 percent. Then, the output voltage is measured with both supply voltages decreased 10 percent. These values are next divided by 100 to determine the corresponding input offset voltages. In turn, the input voltage drift is defined as the difference between these two values, with respect to a 20 percent supply-voltage variation. It is expressed in the form of the following equation:

$$\text{Drift} = \frac{\Delta V_{offset}}{20\%} \tag{4-4}$$

INPUT VOLTAGE DRIFT VERSUS TIME: To measure input voltage drift versus time, the input terminals in Figure 4–17 are short-circuited, and a strip recorder is connected to the output terminals. A typical strip recorder is illustrated in Figure 4–19. The output voltage is then monitored for 24 hours, after which the maximum input voltage offset is noted. In turn, the input voltage drift versus time is defined by the equation:

$$\text{Drift} = V_{in} \text{ off (max)}. \tag{4-5}$$

INPUT NOISE: To measure input noise, the input terminals in Figure 4–17 are short-circuited, and a TVM is connected through a 10-kHz low-pass filter to the output terminals of the op amp. The noise voltage consists of a random mixture of frequencies up to 10 kHz, and is measured in microvolts or millivolts. An rms-indicating TVM is utilized. In turn, the measured value is referred to the input by dividing by 100. Thus, the input noise (in rms value) is given by the following equation:

$$\text{Input Noise} = \frac{\text{Output Noise}}{100} \tag{4-6}$$

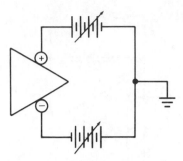

Fig. 4–18 Supply voltage variation for drift measurement.

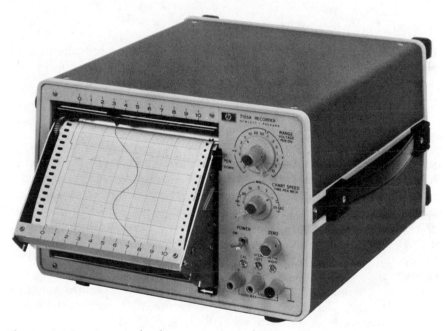

Fig. 4–19 A strip recorder for monitoring voltage variation. *(Courtesy, Hewlett-Packard Co.)*

INPUT CURRENT OFFSET: Input offset current is measured with the standard test circuit depicted in Figure 4–20. This is a unity-gain op-amp configuration in which current owing to offset and drift circulates through the feedback loop. In turn, the output voltage is equal to the voltage across the feedback resistor from which the current may be calculated. Note that it is the isolating property of the op amp which makes it practical to measure the voltage across the 10-meg resistor, even with a VOM. To measure input current offset, the input terminals are short-

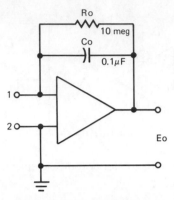

Fig. 4–20   Unity gain amplifier test circuit.

circuited and a TVM or dc oscilloscope is connected across the output terminals. The dc output voltage is measured, and the input current offset calculated in accordance with the following equation:

$$I_{in} \text{ off} = \frac{V_{out}}{10 \times 10^6} \qquad (4-7)$$

INPUT CURRENT DRIFT VERSUS TEMPERATURE: Input current drift versus temperature is measured in essentially the same way as input voltage drift versus temperature. However, the corresponding current drift is calculated from voltage offset measurements. The test circuit depicted in Figure 4–20 is employed, with the input terminals short-circuited, and a TVM or dc oscilloscope connected across the output terminals of the op amp. In turn, the output voltage is measured at 0°C and at 50°C. These values are converted into input current values by dividing the figures by 100 and then by 10×10^6. Next, the current values are subtracted and their difference is expressed as the input current drift versus temperature in accordance with the following equation:

$$\text{Drift} = \frac{\Delta I_{in} \text{ off}}{50°} \qquad (4-8)$$

INPUT CURRENT DRIFT VERSUS SUPPLY: To measure input current drift versus supply-voltage variation, the same basic procedure is utilized as in measurement of input voltage drift versus supply voltage variation. However, input voltage drift values are converted into corresponding input current drift values by dividing the figures by 10×10^6. The test circuit shown in Figure 4–20 is utilized, with the input terminals short-circuited, and a TVM or dc oscilloscope connected to the output terminals of the op amp. The output voltage is measured at a supply-voltage value 10 percent above rated value, and at 10 percent below rated value. Both supply voltages are varied in the test (Figure 4–18). These voltage values are referred to the input by dividing them by 100. Then, they are converted into corresponding current values by dividing each input voltage value by 10^6. Finally, the difference between the two current values is taken and expressed as the drift value in accordance with the following equation:

$$\text{Drift} = \frac{\Delta\, I_{in}\ \text{off}}{20\%} \tag{4–9}$$

Note that when drift measurements are made over a 50° temperature range, it is not necessarily true that the drift per degree will be equal to 1/50 of the total drift value. In other words, drift versus temperature is not necessarily linear. Similarly, when drift measurements are made over a 20 percent supply variation, it is not necessarily true that the drift per percent of supply variation will be equal to 1/20 of the total drift value. As before, the drift versus supply voltage value is not necessarily a linear variation.

REVIEW QUESTIONS

1. What is the function of an op amp in DVM?
2. What is the purpose of the current balancing circuit in Fig. 4–6?
3. What is a current mirror circuit?
4. In Fig. 4–11, what determines the charging current of the integrating capacitor?
5. What is a current mirror type of op amp called?
6. What are some of the uses of current-mirror op amps in automobiles?
7. Draw a diagram of a circuit to measure input voltage drift versus time.
8. What is the input noise in Fig. 4–20 if the output noise measures 50 μvolts?
9. Draw a diagram of a test setup to measure the input offset voltage.
10. State the name of eight op amp measurements that were discussed in Chapter 4 and the formula for each calculation.

5 · Op-Amp Generating Applications

5.1 GENERAL CONSIDERATIONS

Operational amplifiers find extensive application in the generation of precise, controllable signals of various types. Ramp generation was explained in the previous chapter, and we are now in a good position to consider the generation of sine waves, square waves, triangular waves, pulse trains, timed pulses, digital clock pulses, quadrature sine waves, trapezoidal waves, and staircase waveforms. The most basic waveform is the sine wave, and it is the most commonly used test signal. Note that the fundamental characteristic of a sine wave is based upon mathematical forms and operations. In other words, when circuit action is to be described in terms of equations, the choice of the sine wave as the *basic* waveform results in comparatively simple and manageable mathematical expressions. On the other hand, if the seemingly simple square wave is chosen as the basic waveform, the resulting mathematical expressions become prohibitively complicated and unmanageable. This topic is explained in greater detail subsequently.

5.2 OP-AMP SINE-WAVE GENERATORS

Various configurations are used to generate sine-wave voltages. Most of these provide positive feedback for an op amp at a single frequency. Another approach employs a square-wave generator followed by a highly selective op-amp filter arrangement. In other words, a square waveform consists of a large number of harmonically-related sine-wave frequencies. If the harmonics are all filtered out, leaving the fundamental frequency, a sine-wave output is obtained. Some op-amp sine-wave generators employ a combination of basic configurations, such as a combination of Wien-bridge and quartz-crystal oscillator circuitry. Additional functions, such as an automatic gain control (AGC) loop may be included to minimize waveform distortion.

Consider the comparatively simple sine-wave oscillator depicted in Figure 5–1. This arrangement utilizes a slightly detuned parallel-T (twin-T) RC feedback loop whereby the op amp supplies its own input at a chosen frequency. Recall that if the twin-T capacitance and resistance values are chosen for complete rejection of a given frequency, the arrangement operates as an extremely selective bandpass filter. As a bandpass filter, the configuration is stable and does not oscillate. On the other hand, if the feedback loop is slightly detuned by adjustment of the potentiometer in Figure 5–1, a 180° phase shift (positive feedback) will occur and the op amp will oscillate at a frequency given by the equation:

$$f = \frac{1}{2\pi RC} \tag{5–1}$$

where f is in Hertz

R is in ohms

C is in farads

Note that the resistance of the potentiometer in Figure 5–1 should be decreased only to the point that a sine-wave output is obtained. Otherwise, the output waveform will become distorted. This oscillator

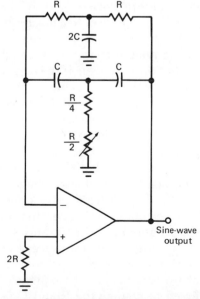

Fig. 5–1 A simple op-amp sine-wave generating arrangement.

configuration is essentially a fixed-frequency design suitable for operation in the audio-frequency range. It is impractical to design the feedback network for variable-frequency operation because all of the R and C values must be changed simultaneously and must track precisely. However, if operation is desired at two or three spot frequencies, a switching arrangement can be utilized with corresponding twin-T networks.

Another basic sine-wave oscillator configuration is shown in Figure 5–2. This is called the Wien-bridge arrangement and its operation is characterized by both positive and negative feedback. Positive feedback occurs through the RC loop to the noninverting input terminal of the op amp. Negative feedback occurs through the resistive voltage-divider circuit to the inverting input of the op amp. As would be anticipated, the circuit will not oscillate unless the positive feedback exceeds the negative feedback. The amount of negative feedback is determined by the setting of the 500-ohm potentiometer. To obtain low distortion in the output waveform, the negative feedback should be almost as great as the positive feedback. Note bulb B_1, which is included to provide output amplitude stability. It functions as an automatic current regulator. If more current tends to flow, the filament becomes hotter and its resistance increases. In turn, more negative-feedback voltage is applied to the op amp.

It is instructive to observe the amplitude and phase relations versus frequency for the Wien-bridge oscillator, as depicted in Figure 5–3. Since the positive feedback loop consists of an RC bandpass filter network, the positive feedback voltage rises to a maximum at the frequency of oscillation. On the other hand, the negative-feedback voltage is not a function of frequency, because it is applied through a resistive feedback loop. Note that oscillation will occur if the negative-feedback voltage level is slightly less than the peak value of the positive feedback voltage. Since the peak of the positive-feedback curve is broad, it might be supposed that the oscillating frequency would not be particularly stable. However, good stability is obtained owing to the rapid change in the phase of the positive feedback voltage through the oscillating frequency. In other words, if the oscillating frequency tends to drift, a phase shift occurs in the positive feedback voltage which reduces the amplitude of oscillation. Since positive feedback always builds up the output to the maximum possible amplitude, this phase variation ensures that the oscillating frequency will be highly stable.

This Wien-bridge op-amp oscillator is generally used in fixed-frequency applications, in the range from 100 to 6,000 Hz. However, if operation is desired at two or three spot frequencies, a switching arrangement can be utilized to change the R and C values as required.

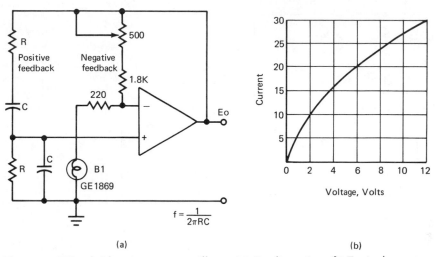

Fig. 5–2 Wien-bridge sine-wave oscillator. **(a)** Configuration; **(b)** Typical tungsten-filament characteristic.

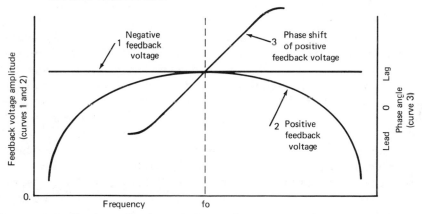

Fig. 5–3 Feedback amplitude and phase relations versus frequency in a Wien-bridge oscillator.

The maximum frequency of oscillation depends on the slew rate of the op amp. Although the op amp itself is not limited to a minimum frequency of oscillation, the lower practical limit of 100 Hz is imposed by the characteristics of the regulator bulb. In other words, the thermal lag of the filament is an essential factor in preventing negative-feedback variation between the start and the end of an individual cycle. Although regulatory action is essential, it must not occur so rapidly that it interferes with the development of the sine wave from its null to its peak.

Another version of the Wien-bridge oscillator is shown in Figure 5–4. This configuration employs a pair of back-to-back zener diodes in-

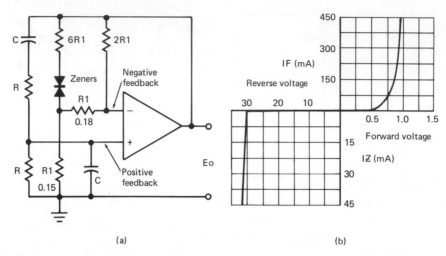

(a)   (b)

Fig. 5–4 Op-amp Wien-bridge sine-wave oscillator with zener-diode stabilization of output amplitude **(a)** Configuration; **(b)** Typical zener-diode characteristic.

stead of a lamp bulb to stabilize the amplitude of the output waveform. If more current tends to flow, the zener diodes draw increased current, or, their effective internal resistance decreases. In turn, more negative-feedback voltage is applied to the inverting input of the op amp. Zener action is much more abrupt than the resistance change in a tungsten filament. Therefore, a swamping resistor 6R1 is connected in series with the zener diodes to minimize waveform distortion while maintaining adequate regulatory action. For this reason also, the zener diodes are connected to the junction of 0.18R1 and 0.15R1, instead of the inverting-input terminal of the op amp. The proportional resistor values stipulated in the negative-feedback loop have been chosen to make the negative-feedback level almost equal to the positive-feedback level, thereby minimizing output waveform distortion. A harmonic-distortion figure of 0.5 percent is typical.

When very low output distortion is required, an active negative-feedback loop can be employed, as depicted in Figure 5–5. Note that this is basically an amplified-AGC arrangement. The chief advantage of this elaborated feedback network is that it permits the oscillator to turn on when the supply voltage is applied, without provision of an undesirable level of positive feedback. By minimizing the positive-feedback voltage required to ensure self-starting, waveform distortion is held to a very small amount. Another feature of the configuration that contributes to a very low percentage distortion is the RC filter C_1R_2. In other words, C_2 provides a time delay in AGC voltage changes, so that

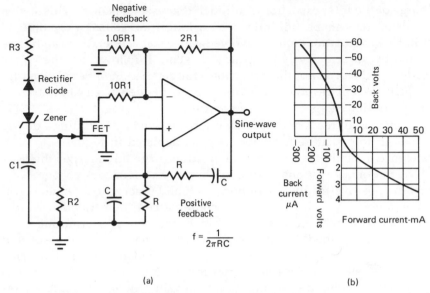

Fig. 5–5 Op-amp Wien-bridge sine-wave oscillator with an active negative-feedback loop. **(a)** Configuration; **(b)** Germanium-diode characteristic; back voltage and current are shown to different scale.

there is no practical interference with the development of the sine wave from its null to its peak. A harmonic-distortion figure of 0.2 percent is typical.

Consider the circuit action in the configuration of Figure 5–5. No current can flow through the rectifier diode until the feedback voltage exceeds the zener threshold. Thus, when the oscillator is starting and building up its output amplitude, the FET has zero gate-source bias voltage. In turn, the drain-source resistance of the FET is comparatively low. This low resistance connects $10R_1$ to ground and enables the op amp to operate at high gain. On the other hand, after the output amplitude builds up sufficiently to exceed the zener threshold, the FET gate voltage falls below the source voltage. Thus, the FET is biased toward turn-off, and its effective drain-source resistance increases. This increases the negative feedback and reduces the gain of the op amp. The net gain around the positive-feedback loop stabilizes at unity.

To summarize briefly, the gain around the positive-feedback loop is greater than unity to enable self-starting of oscillation in Figure 5–5. Then, as the output amplitude increases, the gain is reduced to unity at equilibrium. In turn, the inherent distortion of the system is minimized. There is a slight gain change over each oscillation cycle, particularly at very low operating frequencies. This gain change results from discharge of the filter capacitor C_1 through the reset resistor R_2. This source of distortion can be minimized by a long time constant for the circuit. However, a trade-off is involved, since stable operation can be impaired by an excessively long time constant. It follows that the Wien-bridge oscillator is not the best choice for generation of very low audio frequencies. On the other hand, it is the most widely used configuration for generation of spot audio frequencies.

Increased frequency stability can be realized by including a quartz crystal in the positive-feedback loop, as depicted in Figure 5–6. With reference to Figure 5–3, the crystal functions to greatly sharpen the peak of the frequency-response curve for the positive-feedback voltage. Note that the positive-feedback components R and C serve to attenuate crystal harmonics, and their values are chosen accordingly. In other words, the quartz crystal becomes the dominant frequency-determining component. Like a tuned circuit, the quartz crystal has a phase angle of zero at its resonant frequency, and its internal impedance is resistive. This internal resistance replaces the series resistor R in Figure 5–5. The parallel resistor R in Figure 5–6 should have a value equal to the internal resistance of the crystal, and the parallel capacitor C should have a value given by the equation:

$$RC = \frac{1}{2\pi f_o} \tag{5-2}$$

where f_o is the resonant frequency of the crystal.

5.3 VARIABLE-FREQUENCY SINE-WAVE OSCILLATORS

Variable-frequency sine-wave oscillators employing op amps do not have the Wien-bridge configuration, because the required AGC system becomes objectionably involved. However, a suitable phase-shift configuration, such as shown in Figure 5–7, is well adapted to variable-frequency operation. It is instructive at this point to consider the variable phase-shift configuration depicted in Figure 5–8. Unity gain is provided, with phase shift from input to output controlled by variable resistance. In theory, a 180° phase shift is provided. Note that if R is equal to zero, the input voltage is applied directly to the noninverting input. On the other hand, if R is equal to infinity, the input voltage is applied to the inverting input. Thus, the circuit in (a) provides an adjustable phase variation from 0° to −180°, and the circuit in (b) provides an adjustable phase shift from −180° to −360°.

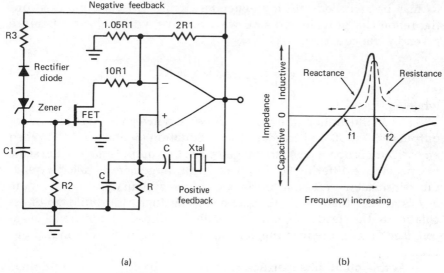

(a)

(b)

Fig. 5–6 Op-amp Wien-bridge sine-wave oscillator with an active negative-feedback loop and a quartz-crystal filter. **(a)** Configuration; **(b)** Quartz-crystal characteristic.

Next, with reference to Figure 5–7, op amp No. 1 employs the foregoing variable phase-shift configuration in a sine-wave generator arrangement with single-resistor variable frequency control. Note that op amp No. 2 utilizes a similar phase-shift configuration, but with fixed resistance. These two phase-shift circuits are connected in series, and are provided with a feedback loop from op amp No. 1 to op amp No. 2. Feedback takes place through an amplitude limiter associated with op amp No. 3. Note that oscillation must occur at the frequency for which the overall phase shift is 360°. In turn, this required phase shift is related to R_1, R_2, and C values according to the equations:

$$\phi_1 = -2 \tan^{-1}\omega R_1 C - 180° \qquad (5-3)$$

$$\phi_2 = -2 \tan^{-1}\omega R_2 C - 180° \qquad (5-4)$$

These phase shifts are added to the 180° phase shift of the amplitude limiter, resulting in an oscillation frequency given by the equations:

$$f = \frac{1}{2\pi C\sqrt{R_1 R_2}} \qquad (5-5)$$

In practice, a 10-to-1 frequency range can be obtained by variation of R_1. When a greater frequency range is desired, a different value of

R_2 may be switched into the generator circuit. Observe that this configuration can provide two sine-wave outputs with a phase difference given by the equation:

$$\phi_1 - \phi_2 = -2 \tan^{-1}\omega RC \tag{5-6}$$

when $R_1 = R_2 = R$.

As an illustration, the phase difference between the two sine-wave outputs will be 90° in accordance with Equation (5–5) if $\omega RC = 1$. When an oscillator is operated so that it generates two outputs having the same frequency but differing 90° in phase, the arrangement is called a quadrature oscillator. Note that initial gain of the system depicted in Figure 5–7 is greater than unity, to enable self-starting. After build-up of oscillation to the steady state, the zener diodes introduce additional negative feedback and reduce the gain so that waveform distortion is minimized.

At this point, it is instructive to consider basic op-amp multipliers and dividers. For example, multiplication or division of a pair of voltages can be accomplished by op amps in high-gain feedback configurations with voltage-controlled resistors or with logarithmic amplifier feedback loops. An arrangement that employs light-dependent resistors is shown in Figure 5–9. Note that op amp No. 2 has a feedback loop that includes a lamp. Op amp No. 2 is operated at nearly zero input voltage. A slightly negative voltage is applied to Z and a slightly positive voltage is applied to Y. The feedback loop for op amp No. 2 energizes the lamp and controls the resistance of light-dependent resistors R_1. Observe that R_2 is a fixed resistor; the current through R_2 is equal to Y/R_2, and the resistance of R_1 is given by the equation:

$$R_1 = \frac{R_2 \cdot Z}{Y} \tag{5-7}$$

Both of the LDR's have the same resistance value, and the output voltage from op amp No. 2 is directly proportional to the voltage applied to the Y terminal, directly proportional to the voltage applied to the X terminal, and inversely proportional to the voltage applied to the Z terminal. In other words:

$$E_o = -\frac{XY}{Z} \tag{5-8}$$

Note that op amp No. 2 inverts the voltage from input to output. Equation (5–7) is called the transfer function for the configuration of

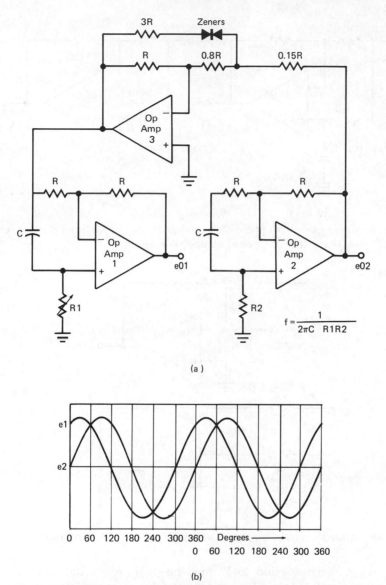

(a)

(b)

Fig. 5–7 Variable-frequency sine-wave oscillator arrangement. **(a)** Configuration; **(b)** Sine waves with a 60° phase difference.

Figure 5–9. It is evident that this transfer function permits analog multiplication or division of input voltages. As an illustration, if Y/Z is set for a ratio of 2, then E_o will be equal to 2X. On the other hand, if Y/Z is set for a ratio of 1/2, then E_o will be equal to X/2. Observe that the voltage applied to Z must be negative for the LDR system to function. In

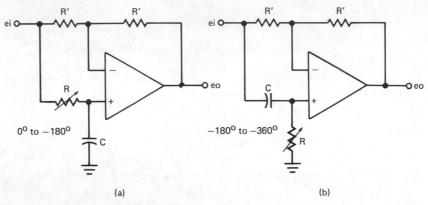

Fig. 5–8 Op-amp variable phase-shift configurations. **(a)** RC input to noninverting terminal; **(b)** CR input to noninverting terminal.

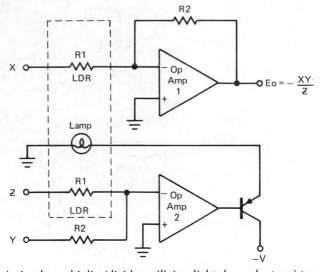

Fig. 5–9 A simple multiplier/divider utilizing light-dependent resistors.

turn, the voltage applied to Y must be positive, so that current Y/R2 flows through R2. The accuracy of multiplication or division provided by this arrangement depends chiefly upon the precision of tracking by the LDR's. An accuracy of 2 percent can be obtained without undue difficulty. More sophisticated op-amp multiplier/divider designs are available, and logarithmic-amplifier configurations provide optimum accuracy, as discussed subsequently.

Next, consider the voltage-controlled op-amp sine-wave quadrature generator depicted in Figure 5–10. Note that the operating fre-

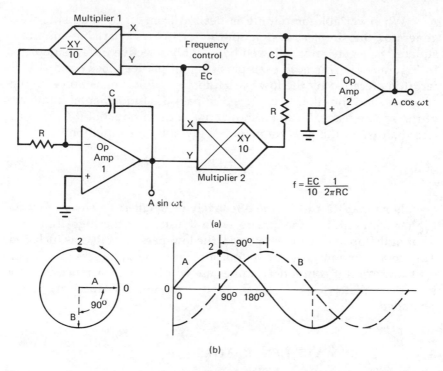

Fig. 5–10 Op-amp sine-wave generator with multipliers in feedback loop. **(a)** Configuration; **(b)** Sine waves in quadrature.

quency is controlled by the voltage value E_c applied to the Y input of multiplier No. 1, and to the X input of multiplier No. 2. Two op-amp integrators are included in the configuration. Observe that multiplier No. 1 has negative gain (polarity inversion) to provide correct feedback polarity. The output from each integrator is multiplied by $E_c/10$. It can be shown that the oscillating frequency is given by the equation:

$$F = \frac{E_c}{10} \cdot \frac{1}{2\pi RC} \tag{5–9}$$

It is often desirable for E_c to vary the oscillating frequency in direct proportion to its value. In turn, it is necessary to add an amplitude stabilization network to the configuration shown in Figure 5–10. For example, one of the AGC arrangements described previously may be employed. A frequency range of 100-to-1 can be obtained when multipliers with adequate dynamic range are utilized. If the multipliers are designed to have sufficiently fast response, an ac control voltage can be employed to obtain a frequency-modulated output from the generator.

When variable amplitude is desired from an op-amp sine-wave generator, the simplest design approach employs a variable-amplitude square-wave generator followed by a highly selective filter, as depicted in Figure 5–11. This is an example of a multiple-feedback bandpass filter; it is preceded by the low-pass filter R_1C_1. Filtering action is highly selective, and the filter is designed to pass the fundamental frequency of the square wave. It can be shown that if the product of R_1C_1 is much less than $1/2\pi f$, the pass frequency is given by the equation:

$$f = \sqrt{\frac{R_2 \parallel R_3}{R_4 \cdot C_2 \cdot C_3}} \cdot \frac{1}{2\pi} \qquad (5\text{--}10)$$

Note that R2 and R3 are effectively in parallel. To ensure that the higher harmonics of the square wave that exceed the high-frequency limit of the op amp will be rejected, the low-pass filter R_1C_1 is included. This configuration provides an output sine wave with less than 1 percent distortion if component values are within close tolerances. In case still lower distortion is desired, another op-amp bandpass stage may be added.

5 . 4 SQUARE-WAVE GENERATORS

A basic op-amp square-wave generator configuration is shown in Figure 5–12. Note that this is an example of a nonlinear application of an op amp, whereas the foregoing sine-wave generator arrangements represented linear applications. The op amp in the square-wave configuration operates in the switching mode, and its output is not directly proportional to its input. Switching action is controlled by charge and discharge of C_2. Note that the op amp swings periodically from a state of positive saturation into negative saturation, and vice versa. Suppose that the op amp is in a state of positive saturation, so that the output voltage is positive. In turn, the op amp is held in positive saturation by the voltage divider R_1–R_2. This circuit action produces the positive half cycle of the square-wave output.

However, the op amp in Figure 5–12 cannot remain in positive saturation indefinitely. Note that C_1 charges in a positive direction through R_3 and R_4. Eventually, the positive voltage at the inverting input will become greater than the voltage at the noninverting input of the op amp. These voltage relations cause the op amp to suddenly switch into negative saturation. Now, the output voltage is negative and C_1 proceeds to discharge (to charge in a negative direction). This circuit action produces the negative half cycle of the square-wave out-

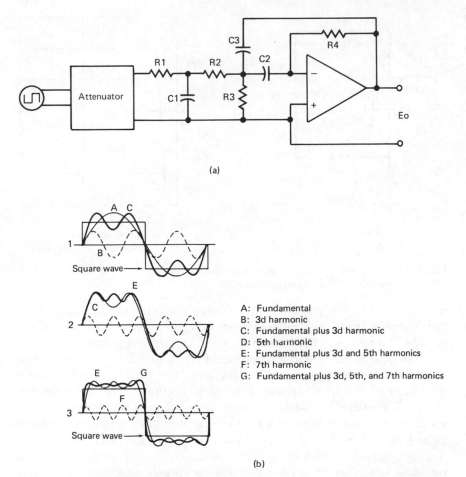

(a)

A: Fundamental
B: 3d harmonic
C: Fundamental plus 3d harmonic
D: 5th harmonic
E: Fundamental plus 3d and 5th harmonics
F: 7th harmonic
G: Fundamental plus 3d, 5th, and 7th harmonics

(b)

Fig. 5–11 A variable-amplitude op-amp sine-wave generator. **(a)** Configuration; **(b)** Square-wave frequency spectrum.

put. Eventually, the negative voltage at the inverting input will become greater than the negative voltage at the noninverting input. These voltage relations cause the op amp to suddenly switch back into positive saturation, and the foregoing circuit actions are repeated.

It is evident that the repetition rate of this astable multivibrator configuration is determined by the time-constant R_3C_1. A moderate variation of repetition rate can be obtained by adjustment of R_3. However, there is a practical lower limit to the value of R_3, and to obtain higher rep rates, the value of C_1 must be reduced. The maximum rep rate is determined by the slew rate of the op amp; this factor also determines the rise time of the square wave at any rep rate. A typical slew

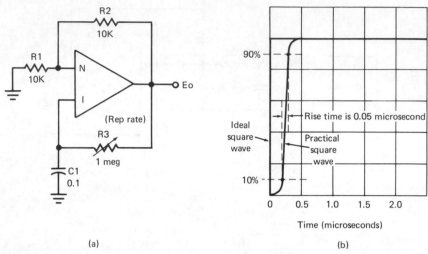

(a)   (b)

Fig. 5–12 Basic op-amp square-wave generator configuration. **(a)** Circuit; **(b)** Example of square-wave rise time.

rate is 0.5 volt per microsecond, although specialized op amps have considerably faster slew rates. If synchronization is desired, sync pulses may be coupled into the noninverting input of the op amp.

Although the astable (free-running) multivibrator is the most common type of square-wave generator, the bistable multivibrator (flip-flop) is also in wide use. A basic configuration is shown in Figure 5–13. Positive feedback occurs at all frequencies within the capability of the op amp. If there is a positive output voltage present, the feedback loop holds the op amp in positive saturation. Or, if there is a negative output voltage present, the feedback loop holds the op amp in negative saturation. Suppose that the op amp is in a state of positive saturation. If a negative pulse voltage is applied to the noninverting input, and this terminal is driven negative, the op amp will suddenly change state and go into negative saturation. Next, if a positive pulse voltage is applied to the noninverting input, and this terminal is driven positive, the op amp will suddenly revert to it positive saturation state. Note that if a second positive trigger pulse is applied, there is no response from the op amp—a negative pulse is required.

Next, consider the monostable (one-shot) multivibrator arrangement depicted in Figure 5–14. It operates in part as an astable multivibrator and in part as a bistable multivibrator. The op amp rests in positive saturation, owing to the voltage divider R_2–R_3. When a negative trigger pulse is applied via C_1, the positive bias to the noninverting input is momentarily reversed, and the op amp suddenly changes state into negative saturation. However, it does not remain in negative sat-

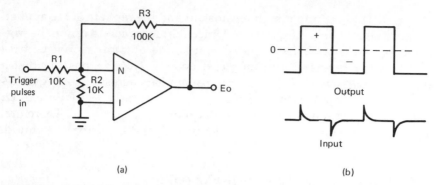

(a)

(b)

Fig. 5–13 A bistable multivibrator (flip-flop) configuration. **(a)** Circuit; **(b)** Waveforms.

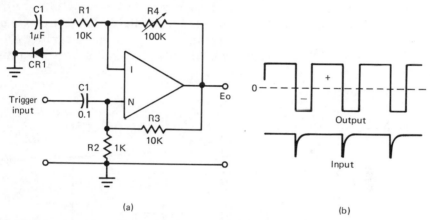

(a)

(b)

Fig. 5–14 A monostable multivibrator arrangement. **(a)** Circuit; **(b)** Waveforms.

uration indefinitely, because C_1 starts to charge through R_1 and R_4. Note that C_1 is initially at ground potential, owing to the bypassing action of CR_1. The voltage divider R_2–R_3 holds the op amp in negative saturation until C_1 charges sufficiently negative that the noninverting input becomes positive (less negative) than the inverting input. Thereupon, the op amp suddenly changes states back into positive saturation. Observe that it must now remain in positive saturation because CR_1 effectively connects R_1 to ground, and the inverting input rests at a less positive potential than the inverting input. When another negative trigger pulse arrives, the monostable cycle is repeated. Note that R_4 varies the charging rate of C_1, and in turn varies the length of the pulse generated by the multivibrator.

It is evident that a monostable multivibrator can operate as a square-wave generator, a rectangular-wave generator, or a pulse generator, depending upon its time constant and the rep rate of the applied trigger pulses. The configuration depicted in Figure 5–14 cannot be triggered by positive pulses; in other words, the op amp cannot be triggered in the reverse direction (reset action). Note in passing that a series of semi-sawtooth waves (ramps) appears across C_1 in Figure 5–14, and that a semi-triangular wave appears across C_1 in Figure 5–12. These waveforms are nonlinear, with exponential curvature. Therefore, more elaborate circuitry is employed when good linearity is required.

5.5 TRIANGULAR-WAVE GENERATORS

An example of a precise square and triangular wave generator is shown in Figure 5–15. This arrangement employs two op amps with comparator feedback around an integrator. A highly linear triangular wave is obtained by utilizing a separate op amp for the integrator. Another advantage of this arrangement is effective control of waveform

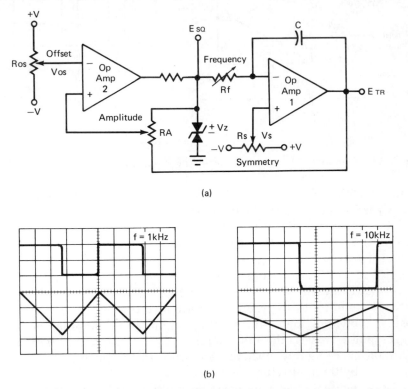

Fig. 5–15 Precise square and triangular-wave generator. **(a)** Circuit; **(b)** Typical output waveforms.

characteristics. In other words, frequency, amplitude, and symmetry controls are available. Note that op amp No. 1 functions as an active integrator, with a feedback loop that includes op amp No. 2 for switching the reference voltage that is integrated. In other words, op amp No. 1 functions as a comparator. Observe that adjustment of the symmetry control serves to increase one integration rate and decrease the other, or vice versa. The peak voltages of the output waveforms are determined by the trip levels of the comparator.

It should be noted that hysteresis feedback occurs through R_A. In op-amp technology, hysteresis is defined as the transfer response lag of a comparator which is controlled by positive feedback. This response lag establishes different trip levels over the operating cycle. That is, a different trip point is caused by the response lag when going from positive to negative saturation, than when going from negative to positive saturation. Switching action occurs when voltage E_{TR} overcomes the hysteresis feedback from E_{SQ}, raising the noninverting input of op amp No. 2 to the offset voltage established by R_{os}. Note that the range of the amplitude control depends on the output swing capability of op amp No. 1 at the upper limit, and on the comparator input offset voltage at the lower limit. Note in passing that a trapezoidal waveform is produced by passing a triangular wave through a limiter.

5.6 RAMP (SAWTOOTH) GENERATORS

A linear ramp and pulse generator employing two op amps is shown in Figure 5–16. Note the similarity of this arrangement to the square and triangular generator depicted in Figure 5–15. An op-amp integrator is utilized with comparator feedback in both configurations. However, the ramp generator circuit in Figure 5–16 includes diode CR1. This diode effectively disconnects the comparator during the positive rise of the ramp waveform. Note also that resistor R_1 has a much smaller value than R, to obtain rapid fall (flyback) of the ramp. As explained previously, hysteresis feedback occurs through R_A, which controls the amplitude of the ramp waveform. The rep rate (frequency) of the ramp and pulse waveforms is controlled by adjustment of the integration resistor R_f.

Next, consider the staircase waveform generator depicted in Figure 5–17. This is a specialized form of ramp generator utilized for multiple-level testing, as in semiconductor curve tracers. Staircase ramp waveforms are also used in sequential control applications. The op amps in the diagram generate a staircase waveform by differentiating and re-integrating a series of square waves in combination with a rectifier that

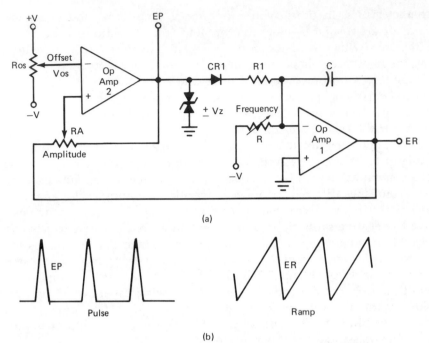

(a)

(b)

Fig. 5–16 Ramp and pulse generator arrangement. **(a)** Circuit; **(b)** Output waveforms.

eliminates the fall of the square wave. Observe that op amp No. 1 has differentiating and rectifying functions. The output from a square-wave generator is applied to the op amp via C_1. On the positive excursion, diode D_1 conducts and the Darlington pair Q1–Q2 is nonconducting. On the other hand, during the negative excursion of the input waveform, diode D_1 does not conduct, and the Darlington pair conducts the differentiated current waveform. In other words, only the negative-going excursion produces an output from Q1–Q2 to op amp No. 2.

Next, op amp No. 2 integrates this applied pulse train, thereby producing the staircase ramp output. Each negative excursion of the square-wave driving waveform charges C_2 another step. However, these output steps cannot continue indefinitely. Note that C_2 and transistors Q_3 and Q_4 function as a reset clamp and go into conduction at the emitter-base breakdown potential of Q_4, as represented by the dashed-line zener diode. In turn, C_2 suddenly discharges through the transistors, and the operational cycle then repeats. The rep rate of the generator is limited by the slewing rate of the op amps, and by the overload recovery rate of Q_4. A slight nonlinearity in the staircase waveform of approximately 0.1 percent results from residual leakage in the reset clamp circuit and from the finite beta values of Q_1 and Q_2.

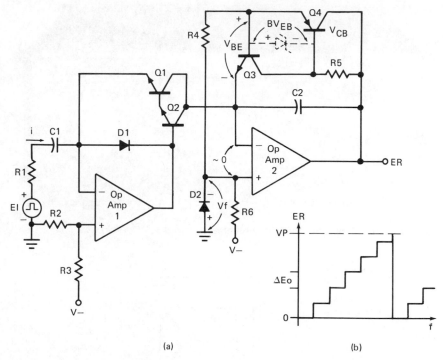

Fig. 5–17 A staircase generator arrangement. **(a)** Configuration; **(b)** Output waveform.

Function generators consist of a combination of various waveform generators such as discussed in this chapter. As an illustration, the generator illustrated in Figure 5–18 provides a choice of nine different waveforms, with a wide range of control over characteristics. This type of generator is used chiefly in design and development work.

5.7 OPERATIONAL VOLTAGE-AMPLIFIER TEST PROCEDURES

Comparatively simple test procedures can be employed to check operational amplifiers for differential current drift, frequency response, rise time, capacitive loading, common-mode input impedance, and full-power response. These test procedures are made as follows.

DIFFERENTIAL CURRENT DRIFT: With reference to Figure 5–19, differential current drift is measured with the configuration shown. No connection is made to the input terminals, and the dc output voltage is measured

Fig. 5–18 An elaborate function generator. (*Courtesy, Wavetek*)

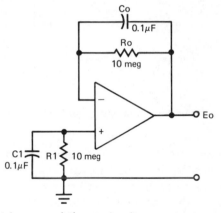

Fig. 5–19 Differential current drift test circuit.

with a TVM or dc scope. In turn, the differential current drift is defined by the equation:

$$\text{Drift} = \frac{\Delta V_{out}}{10 \text{ meg}} \tag{5–11}$$

FREQUENCY RESPONSE: A unity gain noninverting test circuit is depicted in Figure 5–20. This configuration employs 100 percent feedback and provides the most severe test of phase compensation and high-frequency stability. The frequency response of this circuit is limited only by the inherent characteristics of the op amp. A signal generator with a sine-wave output at a 30-mV level is used to drive the op amp. In turn, the output voltage is measured over the rated frequency range of the op

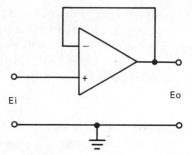

Fig. 5-20 Unity gain noninverting test circuit.

amp with a TVM or scope. The test frequency is increased until the output voltage drops 3 dB below the low-frequency level. This frequency represents the measured bandwidth of the op amp. (The inverting test circuit in Figure 5-21 may also be used.)

RISE TIME: Rise time may be measured with the test circuit depicted in Figure 5-20 or 5-21. A square-wave input voltage is applied at a level of 100 mV p-p. A triggered-sweep scope is used to display the output waveform. It is desirable to employ a square-wave generator that has a considerably faster rise time than the op amp. In such a case, the rise time of the output waveform is practically equal to the rise time of the op amp. Of course, the scope should also have considerably faster rise time than the op amp. In case the scope has a rise time that is marginal, the displayed waveform will have the rise time given by the equation:

$$T_D = \sqrt{T_A^2 + T_O^2} \qquad (5-12)$$

where

T_D is the rise time of the displayed waveform

T_A is the rise time of the op amp

T_O is the rise time of the oscilloscope

In case the oscilloscope has high performance, and the square-wave generator rise time is marginal, the generator and op-amp rise times also combine in accordance with Equation (5-12).

CAPACITIVE LOADING: Capacitive loading, if excessive, can cause instability with configurations such as depicted in Figures 5-20 and 5-21. To determine the tolerable limit of capacitive loading, the op amp is

driven with a sine-wave signal generator at a level of 30 mV. In turn, the
output terminals of the op amp are loaded with a decade capacitor box,
and the output voltage is measured with a TVM or scope. With the signal generator operating near or at the high-frequency limit (−3 dB
point) of the op amp, the capacitive load is increased to the point of
unstable operation. This value of capacitance defines the loading limit.

COMMON-MODE INPUT IMPEDANCE: To measure the common-mode input impedance of an op amp, the test circuit shown in Figure 5–21 is
utilized. The op amp is driven by a sine-wave signal generator operating
at 100 Hz with a level of 1V. A decade resistance box is connected in
series with the "hot" lead from the generator to the op amp. In turn, the
output voltage is measured with a TVM or scope, and the level is noted
with zero series resistance. Next, the series resistance is increased until
the output voltage drops 10 percent. The common-mode input impedance is then given by the equation:

$$Z_{in} = 9R_s \qquad\qquad (5\text{--}13)$$

where R_s is the series resistance that is inserted.

FULL POWER RESPONSE: To measure the full-power response of an op
amp, the test circuit shown in Figure 5–22 is employed. The op amp is
driven with a sine-wave signal generator operating at 100 Hz. In turn,
the output of the op amp is loaded with the desired value of resistance,
and the output voltage is measured with a scope. The signal generator
is set to a level that provides the specified full-power output voltage

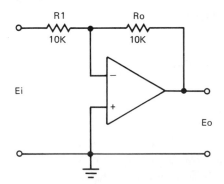

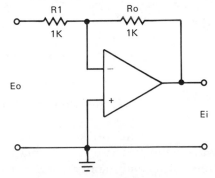

Fig. 5–21 Unity gain test circuit (inverting) with suitable resistance
level for power measure-
ments.

Fig. 5–22 Test circuit for checking full-
power response frequency of
an op amp.

swing from the op amp. Then, the generator frequency is increased until distortion becomes perceptible in the scope pattern. This establishes the full-power response frequency of the op amp.

REVIEW QUESTIONS

1. What is the purpose of the twin-T circuit in Fig. 5–1?
2. What is the frequency of oscillation of the circuit in Fig. 5–1 when $R = 10k\Omega$ and $C = 1.59$ nF?
3. What are the two frequency selection methods in a Wien-bridge oscillator?
4. What limits the lower frequency of the Wien-bridge oscillator in Fig. 5–2?
5. What is the frequency of a phase-shift oscillator when $R1 = 10k$, $R2 = 15k$ and $C = .001\mu F$?
6. What is the oscillating frequency of the circuit in Fig. 5–10 when $E_c = 10$ V, $R = 10$ k and $C = 15.9$ nF?
7. What determines the maximum output frequency of the circuit in Fig. 5–12?
8. In Fig. 5–12, what components determine the repetition rate?
9. What determines the rise time of the square wave in Fig. 5–12?
10. What is a typical slew rate of an op amp?
11. What is the formula for differential current drift?
12. What is the dB drop at the cutoff frequency of the op amp?
13. Draw a diagram of a setup for measuring rise time of an op amp.
14. What is the true rise time of an op amp when $T_0 = 10\mu sec$ and $T_D = 5\mu sec$?
15. How is capacitor loading tested?
16. What is the formula for common-mode input impedances?
17. Draw a circuit for measuring full power response of an op amp.

6 · Specialized
Amplifier
Arrangements

6.1 GENERAL CONSIDERATIONS

Operational amplifiers are used in various specialized applications, such as video amplification, high-frequency amplification, tuned amplification, scaling adders, regenerative amplification, differential input and differential output amplification, gain control, and related arrangements. In analyzing these specialized applications, it is helpful to briefly review two basic feedback circuits. With reference to Figure 6–1, configurations are shown for an inverting amplifier with negative feedback, and for a noninverting amplifier with negative feedback. It is evident that the gain for these two configurations will not be exactly the same, and the difference in gain figures depends upon the relative values of R_0 and R_1. From a practical viewpoint, the gain provided by these configurations is given by the equations:

Inverting configuration:

$$\frac{E_o}{E_i} = \frac{-R_0}{R_1} \tag{6-1}$$

where the minus sign denotes phase inversion.

Noninverting configuration:

$$\frac{E_o}{E_i} = \frac{R_0 + R_1}{R_1} \tag{6-2}$$

As noted previously, op amps employ negative feedback in most applications. Positive feedback is utilized in some applications. Op amps are used without any form of feedback in voltage-comparison applications only. If no feedback is used, an op amp has a frequency characteristic that falls off progressively with increasing frequency, as

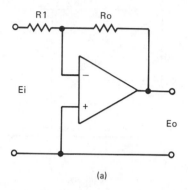 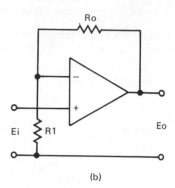

Fig. 6–1 Basic op-amp configurations with negative feedback. **(a)** Inverting configurations **(b)** Noninverting configuration.

exemplified in Figure 6–2(a). On the other hand, if negative feedback is employed, the frequency response becomes much more uniform. In case a large amount of negative feedback is utilized, an op amp will have a flat frequency response out to the limit imposed by the internal design of the device. As an illustration, Figure 6–2(b) shows how flat frequency response can be obtained to 10 MHz. Note the following points:

1. The op amp in the foregoing examples has an internal frequency limit of approximately 10 MHz.
2. Without any feedback, the op amp develops a gain of 60 dB at very low frequencies, with steadily decreasing gain at higher frequencies; at about 10 MHz the op amp has zero gain.
3. When a large amount of negative feedback is utilized, so that the maximum gain is reduced from 60 dB to 6 dB, the op amp then develops uniform gain from very low frequencies to approximately 10 MHz.

Note in passing that positive feedback has the opposite effect on bandwidth that negative feedback provides. In other words, an amplifier that employs positive feedback will have narrower bandwidth than the same amplifier with no feedback. As noted previously, both negative feedback and positive feedback are sometimes used in special applications. It should be emphasized that no feedback and/or frequency-compensating arrangement can be devised that will increase the usable gain of an amplifier beyond its unity-gain frequency. In other words, unity gain occurs at 0 dB, and the unity-gain frequency depicted in Figure 6–2 is approximately 10 MHz.

Although a 6-dB amplifier is suitable for some applications, considerably higher gain is required in other applications. In turn, the op amp must have a correspondingly higher unity-gain figure, if appreci-

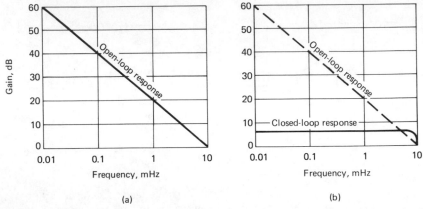

Fig. 6–2 Comparative op-amp frequency responses. **(a)** Response with no feedback; **(b)** Response with large amount of negative feedback.

able bandwidth is to be realized. As an illustration, Figure 6–3 shows a
frequency characteristic for a 50-dB amplifier with flat response from
dc to about 3.5 MHz. In turn, the op amp must have a unity-gain crossover (frequency) of approximately 150 MHz. A 50-dB gain corresponds
to a voltage ratio of 316-to-1, whereas a 6-dB gain corresponds to a voltage ratio of 2-to-1. Note that these are full-power frequency responses,
whereas the unity-gain frequency response is usable only for very small
signal levels. Power capabilities of common types of op amps range
from 100 mW to 750 mW.

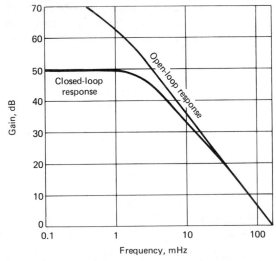

Fig. 6–3 Frequency response for a 50-dB amplifier corresponding to a unity-gain
frequency of 150 MHz.

6.2 DIGITAL PULSE AMPLIFIER

Op amps are used in video amplifiers for general applications, including amplification of digital pulses. As an illustration, Figure 6–4 shows the schematic diagram for an operational amplifier that provides a bandwidth of 3.5 MHz and a gain of 30 dB in the arrangement of Figure 6–5. A gain of 30 dB is equal to a voltage ratio of approximately 32 times. Good stability is provided by phase compensation through a 5-pF capacitor and a 10-k resistor. Note that if phase compensation is not employed, an objectionable peak response will occur at about 4.5 MHz, as depicted in Figure 6–5(c). The input impedance of this video amplifier is 480,000 ohms at low frequencies, decreasing somewhat at higher frequencies.

The pulse-handling capability of the video amplifier depicted in Figure 6–5 is shown in Figure 6–6. Note that the input is a 38-mV 960-ns

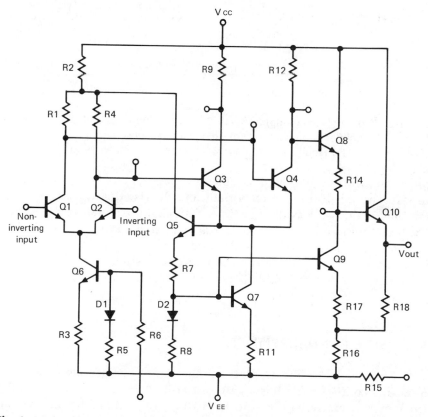

Fig. 6–4 An operational amplifier suitable for digital pulse application. *(Courtesy, RCA)*

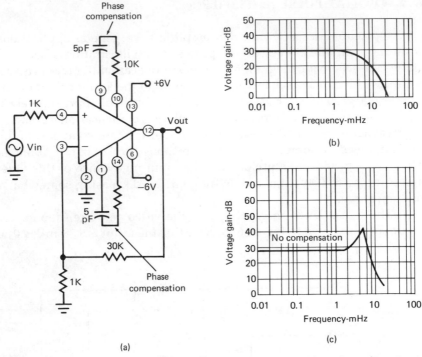

Fig. 6–5 Op-amp video amplifier with 3.5-MHz bandwidth and 30 dB gain. **(a)** Amplifier configuration; **(b)** Frequency response with phase compensation; **(c)** Frequency response with no phase compensation.

pulse, and the output is a 1.1-V pulse (a voltage gain of approximately 30 times). There is a 40-nsec delay time, and the rise time is 125 nsec. The fall time is the same as the rise time. Note that the storage time is zero. On the other hand, if the amplifier is overdriven, a finite storage time occurs. For example, with 20-dB overdrive, a storage time of 160 nsec occurs, with the result that the output pulse is stretched and distorted, as depicted in Figure 6–6(b). Therefore, precautions should be taken to prevent overdrive in most applications.

6.3 WIDE-BAND AMPLIFIER

Next, consider the 42-MHz op-amp amplifier depicted in Figure 6–7. This configuration has a gain of 10 dB, with a 2-dB peaking of the frequency characteristic at the high-frequency end. Both phase-lead and phase-lag compensation are employed. If flat frequency response is desired, a different value of phase-compensating capacitance can be utilized. However, the bandwidth is reduced to 25 MHz when the fre-

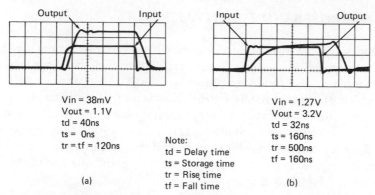

Vin = 38mV
Vout = 1.1V
td = 40ns
ts = 0ns
tr = tf = 120ns

Note:
td = Delay time
ts = Storage time
tr = Rise time
tf = Fall time

(a)

Vin = 1.27V
Vout = 3.2V
td = 32ns
ts = 160ns
tr = 500ns
tf = 160ns

(b)

Fig. 6–6 Video-amplifier response to a digital pulse. **(a)** Low-level response; **(b)** Overdriven response.

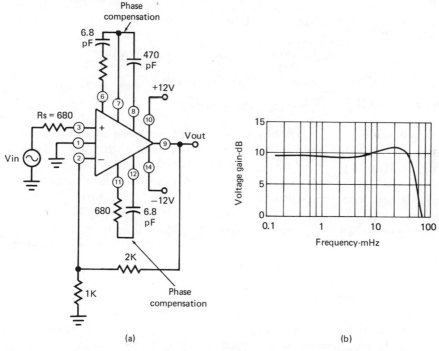

(a)

(b)

Fig. 6–7 Arrangement of a 42-MHz, 10-dB amplifier. **(a)** Configuration; **(b)** Frequency response.

quency response is completely uniform. As noted previously, the function of phase compensation is to reduce or eliminate the tendency for the output voltage of an op amp to shift in phase at high frequencies. This tendency is the result of stray capacitance in the structure of the op amp.

6.4 NARROW-BAND TUNED AMPLIFIER

Op amps can be used with external tuned circuits for narrow-band amplifier operation. As an illustration, Figure 6–8 shows an arrangement for a 100-kHz tuned amplifier with a Q of 33.3 and a half-power bandwidth of approximately 6 kHz. This is an inverting-amplifier configuration and it provides a conventional resonant-circuit frequency response. Although a noninverting amplifier configuration can be used, the frequency response is changed in that the output does not decrease to zero at frequencies far from resonance. The gain equation for the configuration of Figure 6–8 is:

$$\frac{V_{out}}{V_{in}} \quad \frac{-Z_f}{Z_r} \tag{6-3}$$

where Z_f is the feedback impedance

Z_r is the input impedance of the op amp.

6.5 SCALING ADDER

A scaling adder combines and amplifies two or more input voltages, as explained previously. In addition, a scaling adder weights each signal. In other words, weighting involves an artificial adjustment of measurements in order to account for factors which, during normal use of a device, would otherwise differ from the conditions during measurement. As an illustration, background-noise voltages may be weighted for measurement by applying factors to reduce the measured value in inverse ratio to their interference. This is just another way of saying that the input signals to the scaling adder are individually attenuated to specified fractions of their original values. An inverting feedback configuration is employed with an op amp in this scaling-adder application. Weighting operations are possible because there is a virtual ground at the junction of the feedback resistor and the inverting input (Figure 6–9). This virtual ground isolates each signal channel from the other(s).

Weighting operations require that each signal input enter the virtual-ground point through a resistance of such value that its ratio to the feedback resistance is equal to the stipulated weighting factor. In the example, of Figure 6–9, the input signals have sine and square waveforms for purposes of clarity. Note that the weighting factor is 1/10 for the sine wave, and 1/5 for the square wave. In other words, the square-wave signal has a weighting factor which is twice that of the sine-wave

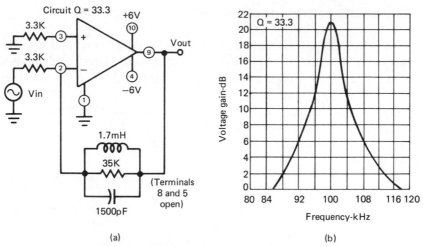

(a)   (b)

Fig. 6–8 A tuned op-amp configuration. **(a)** Circuit; **(b)** Frequency response.

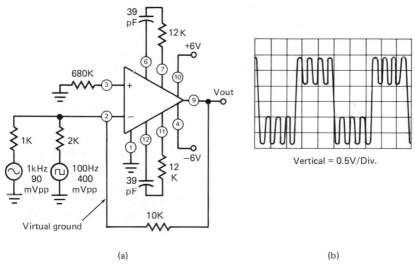

(a)   (b)

Fig. 6–9 Scaling adder arrangement. **(a)** Configuration; **(b)** Output waveform.

signal. Or, the square-wave signal is attenuated 50 percent on a relative basis. Next, observe that the sine-wave signal has a source value of 90 mV p-p, and the square-wave signal has a source value of 400 mV p-p. In effect, the square-wave signal will have an operative source value of 200 mV p-p. Or, the sine-wave signal will have 45 percent of the amplitude of the square-wave signal in the output circuit. These relations are apparent in the output waveform shown in Figure 6–9(b). Note also that the output waveform has an amplitude of 2.8 V p-p. Or, the op amp provides a gain of 200 times.

6.6 REGENERATIVE AMPLIFICATION

An example of regenerative amplification is seen in the pulse-width discriminator arrangement of Figure 6–10. This configuration produces a digital output pulse when the width of an input pulse exceeds a preset value. Note that when no input signal is applied, Q_1 is biased into conduction, holding the input integrator in its reset state. Next, when an input pulse is applied to the base of Q_1, the transistor is cut off and the integrator starts to charge. This charging rate is given by the equation:

$$R_{ch} = \frac{-V}{R_1 C_1} \text{ volts/sec} \qquad (6-4)$$

In turn, the integrator output is a ramp waveform that increases linearly in amplitude with time for the duration of the input pulse. Observe that if the input pulse is sufficiently wide that the output ramp rises to the reference voltage set by R_5, the comparator will regeneratively switch on and will remain on for a period of time equal to the difference between the input pulse width and the reference pulse width given by the equation:

$$T_{ref} = \frac{R_1 C_1 V_{ref}}{-V} \qquad (6-8)$$

where V_{ref} is the value of adjustable voltage at the input to the comparator.

As noted above, in case the input pulse width is less than T_{ref}, no output is obtained from the comparator. Component values indicated in Figure 6–10 permit a range in discrimination from 1 to 100 μs, approximately. When wider pulses need to be accommodated, the value of R_1 may be increased accordingly.

6.7 DIFFERENTIAL INPUT AND DIFFERENTIAL OUTPUT AMPLIFICATION

All op amps have differential input design, although they are commonly operated with single-ended input. As has been explained previously, either the inverting or the noninverting input may be driven, with the other input returned to ground. Most op amps have single-ended output design, although a few are designed with differential output. Differential output is desirable for direct driving of electro-

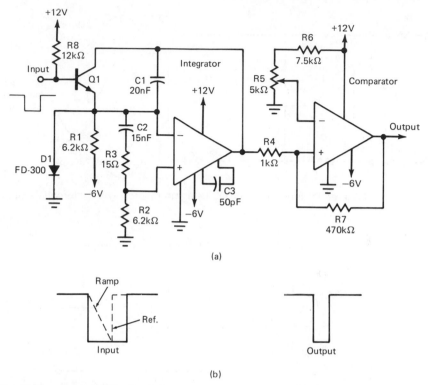

(a)

(b)

Fig. 6–10 Pulse-width discriminator that uses positive feedback. **(a)** Circuit; **(b)** Pulse relations.

mechanical devices such as solenoids and indicators which require a greater voltage swing than provided by single-ended output types of op amps. With reference to Figure 6–11, a basic configuration is shown for push-pull input and push-pull output with this type of op amp. Note that negative feedback is applied to both input terminals. Although a 30-volt (±15-volt) power supply is employed, an output voltage swing of 50 volts peak-to-peak is obtained. This swing is attainable because the 30-volt power supply contributes its voltage to both the inverting-output and the noninverting-output sections.

Note that the output signal from the op amps in Figure 6–11 can be applied to a floating load, both ends of which operate above ground potential. Next, suppose that it is desired to obtain differential-output operation with op amps that have single-ended output. In such a case, the configuration shown in Figure 6–12 may be employed. This is an arrangement that utilizes single-ended input. As a practical note, this arrangement has considerably less useful bandwidth than that of the configuration in Figure 6–11. Less effective bandwidth is available be-

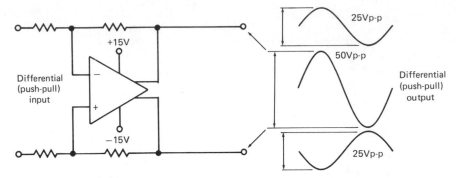

Fig. 6–11 Differential input and output, using an op amp with differential-output design.

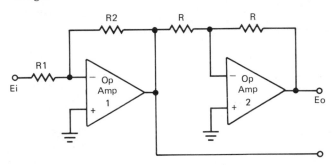

Fig. 6–12 Two conventional op amps provide double-ended output with single-ended input.

cause each of the op amps introduces phase shift at higher frequencies, and these phase shifts are additive. By way of comparison, observe the configuration depicted in Figure 6–13. A pair of op amps are employed in a circuit that provides both differential input and differential output. Since phase shifts are not additive, it provides greater bandwidth than the arrangement in Figure 6–12; it also provides higher input impedance. As an operating note, the driving source in Figure 6–13 must be center-tapped and returned to ground to complete the input bias-current circuit.

6.8 AMPLIFIER WITH AUTOMATIC GAIN CONTROL

Operational transconductance amplifiers have a variable transconductance characteristic as exemplified in Figure 6–14. The transconductance value is determined by the amplifier bias current (ABC). In turn, this characteristic makes an OTA useful in an AGC amplifier. With

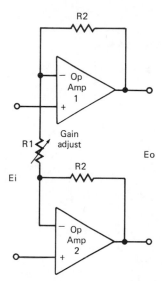

Fig. 6–13   Two conventional op amps provide double-ended output and double-ended input.

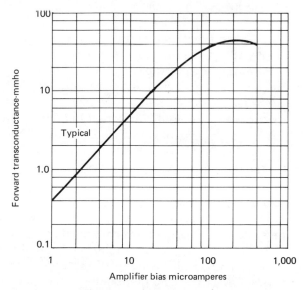

Fig. 6–14   Typical transconductance characteristic for an OTA.

reference to the block diagram shown in Figure 6–15, the output signal from the amplifier is detected (rectified) and passed through a network comprising a low-pass filter. This filter changes the pulsating-dc output from the detector-amplifier into smooth dc, and also imposes a certain time delay in AGC action. The amount of time delay is determined by

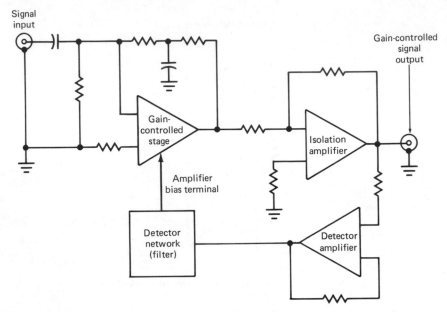

Fig. 6–15   Op amp general-purpose amplifier with agc.

the time-constant of the filter. For control action, the AGC voltage is polarized so that the ABC decreases as the signal input voltage increases. In turn, the transconductance of the gain-controlled stage is reduced, maintaining the output signal amplitude essentially constant. Low-frequency negative feedback is provided for the gain-controlled stage to stabilize the system and prevent "hunting". In other words, the ABC changes must always represent negative feedback at all frequencies.

6.9   OP-AMP MODULATOR ARRANGEMENT

The transconductance characteristic depicted in Figure 6–14 also finds application in amplitude modulation from dc to the upper cutoff frequency of the system. A single OTA is employed in the configuration of Figure 6–16(a). Note that the carrier signal is applied to the differential input of the op amp, and the modulating signal current is added to the quiescent ABC. A carrier and modulating frequency capability in excess of 20 kHz is provided by a typical OTA. Waveforms produced by modulator action are exemplified in Figure 6–16(b) for a carrier frequency of 10 kHz and a modulating frequency of 500 Hz. Next, Figure 6–16(c) shows the waveform obtained with a 500-Hz carrier and a 10-kHz modulating frequency.

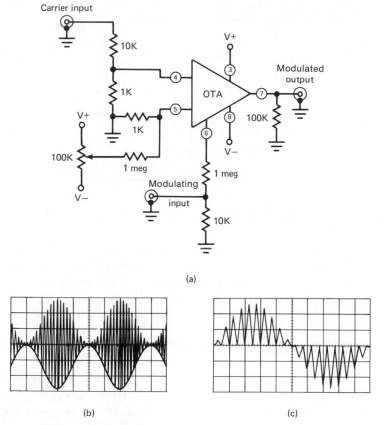

(a)

(b)　　　　　　　　　　　　　(c)

Fig. 6–16　OTA amplitude-modulator arrangement. **(a)** Configuration; **(b)** Output waveform, 10 kHz/500 Hz; **(c)** Output waveform, 500 Hz/10 kHz.

6.10　BOOTSTRAPPED AMPLIFIER OPERATION

To obtain extremely high input impedance to an op amp, a bootstrapping feedback configuration may be employed. This technique uses output voltage of the same polarity as the input voltage to inject a current into the input circuit which is equal to the current drawn from the driving source in the absence of feedback. In turn, the source does not supply any driving current and the input impedance becomes effectively infinite. With reference to Figure 6–17, the input voltage is applied to the noninverting terminal of the op amp. Bootstrapping is provided by positive feedback through R_2, R_3, and R_4. Adjustment of the value of R_3 permits the input current demand to be precisely bal-

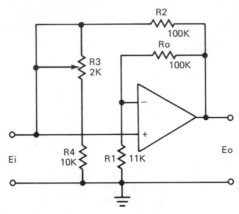

Fig. 6–17 A bootstrapped amplifier configuration.

anced out (supplied by) the feedback current. At balance, the input impedance of the op amp is effectively infinite. Note that excessive bootstrapping will cause instability, since the amplifier will then supply its own input and break into oscillation.

6.11 DC LEVEL-SHIFTING PRINCIPLES

At this point, it is instructive to consider basic dc level-shifting principles employed in op amps. As seen in Figure 6–4, an op amp is dc-coupled throughout. The dc voltage level of simple cascaded dc-coupled amplifiers rises through successive stages and approaches the power-supply voltage. Therefore, cascaded dc-coupled stages in an op amp are supplemented by provisions to compensate for this voltage rise, so that there will be no dc offset in the output circuit. Figure 6–18 shows the simplest method to obtain a downward shift in dc level. This configuration employs an emitter-follower stage between one differential-amplifier stage and the next differential-amplifier stage. The constant-current source I_o and the resistance R_c are chosen so that the collector voltage at Q_1 is equal to $2V_{BE}$, where V_{BE} is the voltage drop across the base-emitter junction of Q_1. Thus, the collector voltage at Q_1 is equal to two forward-biased voltage drops above the emitter voltage of Q_1. In turn, the voltage drop across the base-emitter junction of Q_2 makes the base voltage of Q_3 equal to the base voltage of Q_1. Accordingly, this arrangement permits similar stages to be cascaded with the collector and base voltages remaining at the same dc level.

The chief disadvantage of the foregoing arrangement is that the signal-voltage swing is comparatively limited. Op amps designed for

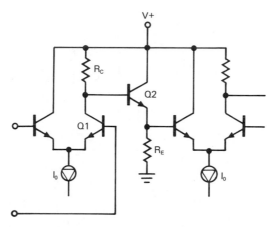

Fig. 6–18   A dc level-shifting circuit utilizing an emitter follower.

comparatively large voltage swings may use the level-shifting configuration shown in Figure 6–19. Observe that the differential stages employ NPN transistors, whereas a PNP transistor is utilized as a level
shifter between stages. Downward shift of collector voltage between
Q_1 and the base of Q_3 is obtained via the collector-emitter voltage of
Q_2. Note that Q_3 is an effective collector load for Q_2. Although a large
signal-voltage swing is obtained, this arrangement has the disadvantage
of poorer high-frequency response than the configuration depicted in
Figure 6–18. In other words, an integrated PNP transistor has inherently
poorer high-frequency response than an integrated NPN transistor.

Another dc level-shifting arrangement that provides better high-
frequency response with a PNP transistor is shown in Figure 6–20.
Note that the level-shifting PNP transistor is operated in the common-
base mode. A common-base configuration has inherently better high-
frequency response. Transistors Q_2 and Q_3 comprise a differential pair,
and the collector signal current of Q_1 produces an equal emitter signal
current in Q_4. Although better high-frequency response is obtained
with this arrangement, it has the disadvantage of single-ended input
only.

Next, consider the technique utilized in designing the output stage
of an op amp, so that there is zero shift in dc level between the input and
the output terminals. With reference to Figure 6–21, Q_1 functions as an
input buffer, and Q_2 provides a constant-current source for Q_1. A shift
in dc level results from the voltage drop across R_1, owing to the collector current of Q_2. Note that the emitter of Q_3 is bootstrapped to the
emitter of Q_2. Feedback from Q_2 through R_3 causes a decrease in the
voltage drop across R_1 during negative-going output swings, and an

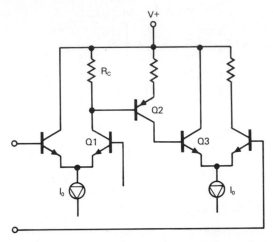

Fig. 6–19 A dc level-shifting circuit that employs a PNP transistor.

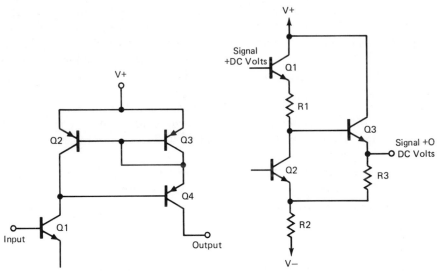

Fig. 6–20 A dc level-shifting circuit with better high-frequency response.

Fig. 6–21 A dc level-shifting output network.

increase across R_1 during positive-going output swings. This configuration provides considerable voltage gain, a high input impedance, a low output impedance, and an output swing that nearly equals the supply voltages, while producing the necessary shift in dc level.

Forward-biased diodes are also used for shifting dc levels in op-amp circuitry. With reference to Figure 6–22, several forward-biased diodes, or a zener diode, may be connected in series between the col-

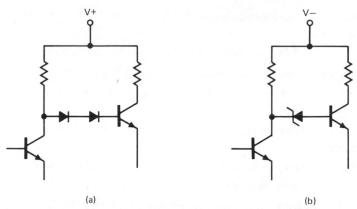

Fig. 6–22 dc level-shifting diode circuits. **(a)** With forward-biased diodes; **(b)** With zener diode.

lector and base of cascaded stages. The chief disadvantage of this arrangement is the impedance that it introduces into the signal path. Therefore, transistor level shifters are generally preferred.

6.12 MOUNTING AND HANDLING OPERATIONAL AMPLIFIERS

When op amps are mounted in a manner that requires bending of the leads, it is important that the lead be supported and clamped between the bend and the package seal, and that bending be done with care to avoid damage to the plating on the lead. The radius of the bend should always be greater than the diameter of the lead. In the case of rectangular leads, the radius of the bend should always be greater than the thickness of the lead. Note that the ends of the bent leads should be straight to ensure proper insertion through holes in the printed-circuit board. Overheating must be avoided during soldering operations, or the op amp will be damaged.

REVIEW QUESTIONS

1. What is the gain of an op amp, noninverting, when $R_0 = 10$ M ohm and $R_1 = 10$ k ohm?

2. What happens to the gain of an op amp (without feedback) as the frequency increases?

3. What is the relationship between negative feedback and the bandwidth of an op amp?

4. How does positive feedback affect the bandwidth of an op amp circuit?

5. What are the power capabilities of common types of op amps?

6. What is the purpose of using phase compensation in the circuit in Fig. 6–5?

7. What causes the output voltage of an op amp to shift in phase at high frequencies?

8. What is the equation of the voltage gain in the circuit in Fig. 6–8?

9. What is a scaling adder?

10. What is meant by the term "weighting of a signal"?

11. How is a 50 volt peak-to-peak signal obtained in the circuit in Fig. 6–11?

12. What is one useful purpose of the OTA?

13. What is the purpose of bootstrapping an op amp circuit?

14. Compare the high-frequency response of an integrated NPN transistor to that of an integrated PNP transistor.

15. What are some precautions that should be taken with an op amp?

7 · Specialized Op-Amp Applications

7.1 TIME-DIVISION MULTIPLEXING

Time-division multiplexing involves one of the important specialized applications of op amps. Multiplexing is the process of combining several measurements (waveforms) in transmission over a single line or in a single channel. Two principal types of multiplexing are employed. Time-division multiplexing uses a time-sharing pattern of pulsed samples from the transmitted waveforms. Frequency-division multiplexing utilizes data from each channel (waveform) to modulate individual subcarriers which are then modulated on the carrier wave. Op-amp application is chiefly concerned with time-division multiplexing. Figure 7–1 pictures four ways in which a sine waveform may be sampled by pulses. These are pulse-amplitude modulation (PAM), pulse-duration or pulse-width modulation (PDM), pulse-position modulation (PPM), and pulse-code modulation (PCM). Note that PAM employs analog sampling, whereas the other forms of modulation utilize digital sampling. Each of these sampling signals can be passed through suitable demodulators to reconstitute the original unsampled signal.

With reference to Figure 7–2, a PAM waveform can be processed by a low-pass filter to recover the original waveform. The time-constant of the filter is chosen so that the pulse frequency falls beyond the cutoff frequency of the filter, whereas the envelope frequency falls within the cutoff frequency of the filter. More elaborate demodulating arrangements are required to recover the original waveform when PDM, PPM, or PCM is used. At this point, it is instructive to observe how time-division multiplexing is applied to PAM. In Figure 7–3 three different waveforms are being sequentially sampled. A three-channel gated amplifier comprising three OTA's is utilized, as depicted in Figure 7–4. Each channel is sequentially activated by a strobe (gating) waveform to pass its input waveform with a gain of approximately 20 dB. Figure 7–5 shows the timing of the strobe waveform. Note that a common feed-

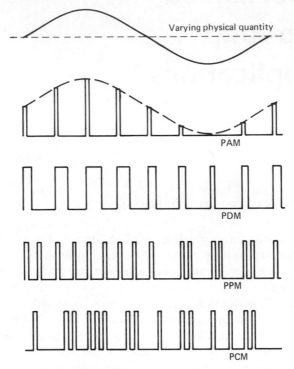

Fig. 7–1 Waveform sampling by various types of pulse modulation.

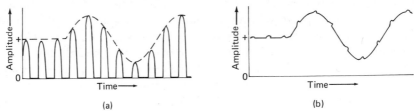

Fig. 7–2 Processing of sampled waveform. **(a)** Input to low-pass filter; **(b)** Output from low-pass filter.

back network is used for all three op amps. This is a practical configuration because the input impedance of an OTA is very high when it is biased "off".

Position control of each output waveform in Figure 7–4 is accomplished by adding an adjustable dc component to the input waveform. This is basically an offset adjustment connected to the inverting input of each op amp. Note that each channel is gated on by cutting off a normally-saturated transistor connected in shunt to the op-amp bias-current terminal. By adding a different value of dc component to each input

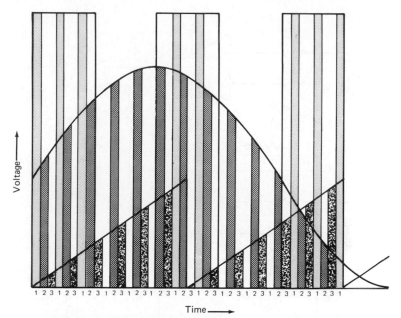

Fig. 7–3   Example of time-division multiplexing.

waveform, the three output waveforms can be displayed one above the other on the screen of an oscilloscope. Note that the sampling rate depicted in Figure 7–3 is comparatively slow—considerable distortion would be observed in the reconstituted waveforms displayed on the scope screen. Therefore, in practice, a sufficiently rapid sampling rate is employed to provide substantially undistorted output waveforms. The chief disadvantage of rapid sampling rates is the comparatively large bandwidth that is required in each channel.

7.2   SAMPLE-HOLD-READ CONFIGURATION

Some sampling arrangements are designed to hold the value of the sample for a certain length of time before it is displayed or otherwise utilized. A pair of OTA's is employed in this application, as depicted in Figure 7–6. C_1 is the charging capacitor that holds the sampled value until a strobe-read pulse is applied. Thereupon, an output pulse is produced which has the same amplitude as the sampled value. Next, when the next strobe-sample pulse is applied, C_1 is charged or discharged in accordance with the amplitude of the input signal at that instant. Note that both OTA's are biased off unless a strobe pulse is present. C_2 is a small stabilizing capacitor. The maximum sampling rate is determined

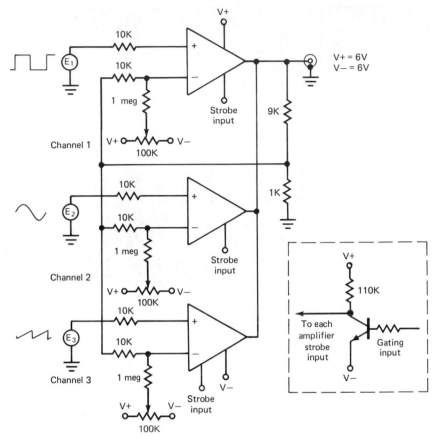

Fig. 7–4 A three-channel gated-amplifier arrangement.

by the slew rate of the OTA's. Note that both OTA's operate as voltage followers.

7.3 SAMPLE-HOLD-COMPARE CONFIGURATION

Other sampling arrangements are designed to hold the value of a sample while it is being compared with a reference voltage. A pair of OTA's is utilized in this application, as shown in Figure 7–7. When a strobe-sample pulse is applied to the charging OTA, C_1 is quickly charged to the amplitude of the input signal. Next, when a strobe-compare pulse is applied to the comparator OTA, the voltage being held by C_1 determines the amplitude of the resulting output pulse. Then, when the next strobe-sample pulse is applied, C_1 is charged or discharged in

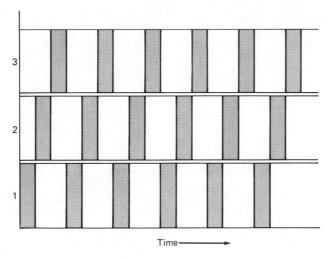

Time⟶

Fig. 7–5 Timing of the strobe waveform.

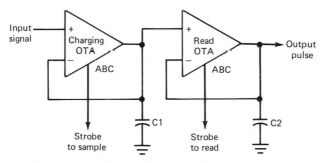

Fig. 7–6 Two OTA's in a sample-hold-read configuration.

accordance with the amplitude of the input signal at that instant. The charging OTA is biased off unless a strobe-sample pulse is present. Similarly, the comparator OTA is biased off unless a strobe-compare pulse is present; however, the comparator OTA does not operate in the linear mode. In other words, when it is gated on, the OTA will go either into positive saturation or into negative saturation, depending upon the comparative amplitudes of the voltage on C_1 and the reference voltage.

7.4 FOUR-QUADRANT MULTIPLIER CONFIGURATION

Previous treatment of basic op-amp multiplier action has shown how an input signal can be multiplied by a constant such as 2, $\sqrt{3}$, π, and so on. We are now in a good position to consider multiplication by

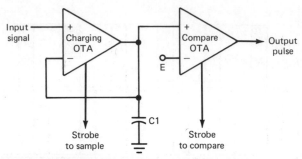

Fig. 7–7 A sample-hold-comparison configuration.

either positive or negative numbers, and multiplication of an algebraic function by another algebraic function. The basis of four-quadrant multiplication is pictured in Figure 7–8. Observe that x and y are both positive in the first quadrant; x is negative and y is positive in the second quadrant; x and y are both negative in the third quadrant; x is positive and y is negative in the fourth quadrant. Note that if x is squared (multiplied by itself), the product falls in the first and second quadrants

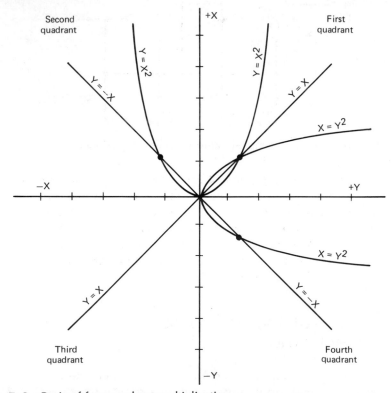

Fig. 7–8 Basis of four-quadrant multiplication.

(y is always positive). Again, if y is squared, the product falls in the first and fourth quadrants.

Three OTA's are utilized in the basic configuration for a four-quadrant multiplier as depicted in Figure 7–9. Op amp No. 1 is connected as an inverting amplifier for the x signal. Op amp No. 2 is connected as a noninverting amplifier. Thus, the output from op amp No. 1 will have the opposite algebraic sign compared to the output from op amp No. 2. Op amp No. 3 is connected as a unity-gain inverting amplifier, and supplies bias for op amp No. 1. It can be shown that the output voltage from this configuration is equal to the product of input voltages x and y, regardless of their signs. Thus, if input x is $+1$ unit and input y is -2 units, the output will be equal to -2 units. Again, if input x is $\sin 2\pi ft$ (a function of time), and input y is also $\sin 2\pi ft$ (the same function of time), the output will be equal to $\sin^2 2\pi ft$ (the square of the input function).

Next, Figure 7–10 shows a detailed four-quadrant multiplier configuration, with the adjustments required for precise differential input and equalizing the gains of op amps No. 1 and No. 2. Typical signal multiplications are pictured in Figure 7–11. Thus, when a triangular waveform is fed to both the x input and the y input, the output wave form is effectively the function $y = x^2$. This is parabolic waveform as seen in Figure 7–11(a). Note that the triangular waveform has both

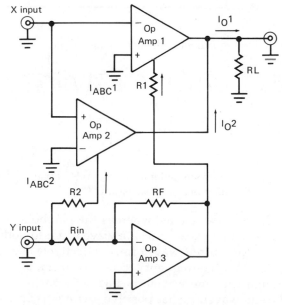

Fig. 7–9 Basic configuration for a four-quadrant multiplier.

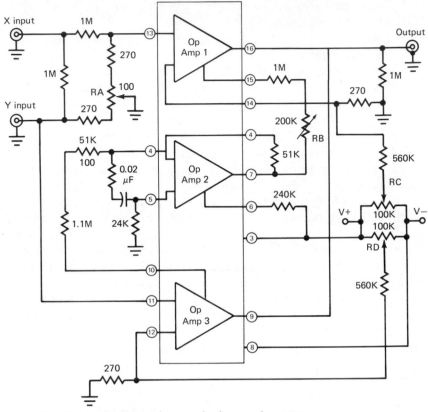

Fig. 7–10 Detailed four-quadrant multiplier configuration.

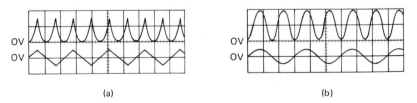

(a)   (b)

Fig. 7–11 Examples of waveform multiplications. **(a)** Squaring of a sawtooth waveform; **(b)** Squaring of a sine waveform.

positive and negative excursions, whereas the parabolic waveform has
positive excursions only. Next, if a sine wave is fed to both the x input
and the y input, the output waveform is effectively the function $y =$
$\sin^2 2\pi ft$. This is a double-frequency sine waveform, as seen in Figure
7–11(b). Although the sine waveform has both positive and negative
excursions, the $\sin^2$ waveform has positive excursions only.

It is instructive to observe how an op-amp multiplier can be applied to simulate suppressed-carrier amplitude modulation. An example of amplitude modulation is depicted in Figure 7–12. The equation of the modulated carrier is written:

$$e = E_o(1 + m \sin 2\pi f_s t) \sin 2\pi f t \qquad (7\text{–}1)$$

where E_o is the peak value of the unmodulated carrier

m is the percentage of modulation

f_s is the modulating frequency

f is the carrier frequency

When this equation is expanded, it takes the form:

$$e = E_o \sin 2\pi f t + \frac{mE_o}{2} \cos 2\pi (f - f_s)t - \frac{mE_o}{2} \cos 2\pi (f + f_s)t \qquad (7\text{–}2)$$

Next, if the carrier term is removed, the suppressed-carrier waveform will be given by the generalized equation:

$$e = \frac{1}{2} \cos (x - y) - \frac{1}{2} \cos (x + y) \qquad (7\text{–}3)$$

Observe that Equation (7–3) has the equivalent form:

$$(\sin x)(\sin y) = \frac{1}{2} \cos (x - y) - \frac{1}{2} (\cos x + y) \qquad (7\text{–}4)$$

Therefore, the end result of suppressed-carrier amplitude modulation can be obtained by using a four-quadrant op-amp multiplier to develop the product of $(\sin x)(\sin y)$. In other words, the waveform $\sin 2\pi(f - f_s)t$ is applied to the x input, and the waveform $\sin 2\pi(f + f_s)t$ is applied to the y input. Note in passing that an AM waveform from which the carrier has been removed has an envelope frequency that is double the envelope frequency of the complete AM waveform. This circumstance follows from Equation (7–4), in which a $\sin^2$ term appears. With reference to Figure 7–11(b), it was previously noted that a $\sin^2$ waveform has a double frequency with comparison to the sin waveform. Finally, Figure 7–13 shows the output waveform that is obtained in simulated suppressed-carrier modulation of a sine wave with a triangular wave.

Four-quadrant op-amp multipliers are employed in analog computers. In turn, it is instructive to consider the basic characteristics of

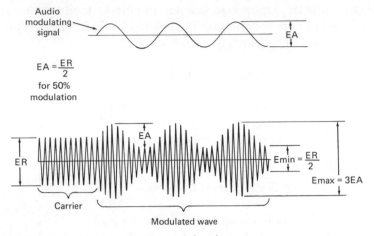

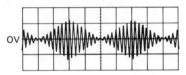

Fig. 7–12 Example of an amplitude-modulated sine wave.

Fig. 7–13 Suppressed-carrier modulation of a sine wave with a triangular wave.

analog computation. An analog is also called an analogy or a model. In particular, an analog computer is a physical or electronic model of a mathematical operation or operations. As an illustration, an analog computer can be employed to solve problems involving Ohm's law or Newton's law, using the same op-amp configuration. In other words, Ohm's Law and Newton's law are expressed by similar equations:

$$E = IR \qquad (7\text{–}5)$$

$$F = MA \qquad (7\text{–}6)$$

In turn, with reference to Figure 7–14, an electric circuit described by Ohm's law is analogous to a moving object described by Newton's law, and both are analogous to the action of a four-quadrant op-amp multiplier. These analogies enable us to solve Equations (7–5) and (7–6) by means of a suitably programmed multiplier. In these applications, the terms I, R, M, and A may be variables, or some may be constants and others variables, or all may be variables. In any case, proportional voltages are applied to the x input and the y input of the four-quadrant op-amp multiplier to obtain the product values of the input voltages. In practical situations, an analog computer often accepts data from remote

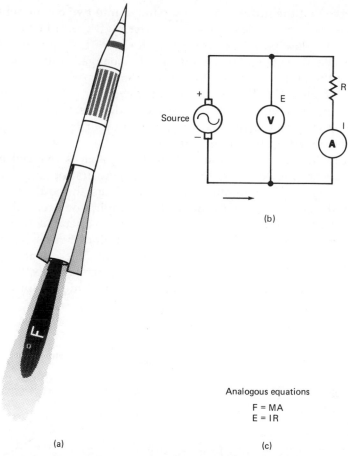

Analogous equations

$$F = MA$$
$$E = IR$$

(a)   (c)

Fig. 7–14 Example of analogies. **(a)** Acceleration of a mass by reaction of a force; **(b)** Motion of electric charge by application of a voltage; **(c)** Mathematical analogs of the foregoing physical systems.

sensors and processes the data to obtain useful answers. As an illustration, precise aiming of an anti-aircraft gun requires the rapid processing of data from several sensors.

7.5 CHOPPER-STABILIZED OPERATIONAL AMPLIFIERS

When very low drift op-amp arrangements are required, chopper stabilization is commonly employed. Basically, chopper stabilization employs a dc amplifier to amplify ac signals that have been rectified, and ac signals that have not been rectified. With reference to Figure 7–

15, observe that the input signal is separated into two components by a high-pass filter and a low-pass filter. The high-pass filter comprises R_1C_1, and the low-pass filter comprises R_2C_2. In turn, the output from the low-pass filter is chopped and thereby changed into an ac signal. Note that the output from the low-pass filter consists of dc and ac frequencies of a few Hz. The output from the chopper is stepped up by an op amp, and is then rectified (converted to dc). Next, both the output from the rectifier or demodulator and the output from the high-pass filter are stepped up by another op amp.

It can be shown that the drift in the system is reduced by this chopper technique by the gain of the chopper, first op amp, and demodulator. Since this gain can be made quite large, the equivalent input drift is reduced essentially to that of the chopping device. Various devices are utilized for chopping, such as a light-operated LDR (light-dependent resistor), a bipolar resistor, or a unipolar resistor. Only an inverting input is available in a chopper-stabilized amplifier. Although the arrangement is comparatively elaborate and costly, it finds extensive application in systems that require very high stability.

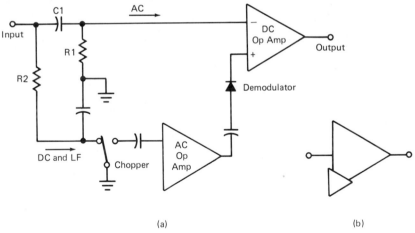

Fig. 7–15 Plan of a chopper-stabilized op amp. **(a)** Configuration; **(b)** Symbol.

7.6 VARACTOR TYPE OF OP AMP

Another type "chopper" op amp is called a varactor op amp, as depicted in Figure 7–16. A varactor is a reverse-biased diode that operates as a capacitor. Its junction capacitance depends upon the value of applied bias voltage. In a varactor op amp, a pair of varactor diodes operate in the arms of an ac bridge which is normally balanced and has

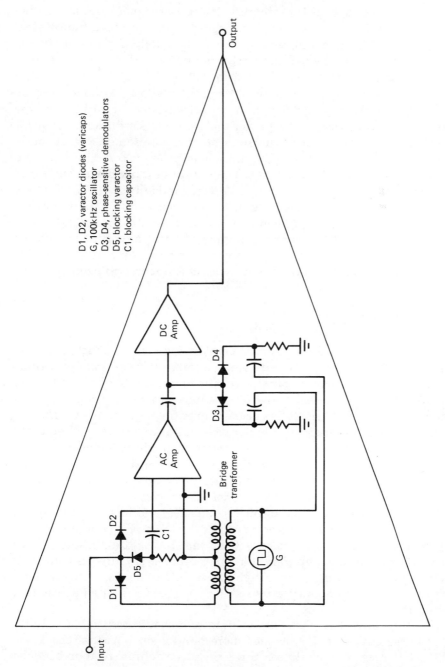

Fig. 7–16 Plan of a varactor operational amplifier.

D1, D2, varactor diodes (varicaps)
G, 100kHz oscillator
D3, D4, phase-sensitive demodulators
D5, blocking varactor
C1, blocking capacitor

no output. However, when an input signal is applied to the varactor op amp, the varactor capacitances become unequal, and the bridge becomes unbalanced. In turn, there is an output signal from the bridge which is amplified and then demodulated to reproduce the original waveform. The demodulated signal is finally stepped up through a dc amplifier. Note that when the bridge is unbalanced, a 100-kHz output is applied to the phase-sensitive demodulator.

A varactor operational amplifier converts low-frequency and dc signals to a higher frequency in the varactor bridge. In turn, amplification can be provided at a frequency that introduces minimum transistor noise. Note that transistor noise is most troublesome at frequencies below 500 Hz. Since most of the noise in a system is contributed by the input stage, it is helpful to employ a low-noise input stage. The input impedance of the varactor op amp depicted in Figure 7–16 is 10^{14} ohms —an extremely high value. Note that only a noninverting input is available. The bias-current demand of the varactor op amp is extremely small—0.01 pA in this example. Chopping (switching) action introduces a noise component called flicker noise. A varactor op amp has considerably less flicker noise than other types of chopper-stabilized op amps.

7.7 BODE PLOTS

Most op-amp arrangements employ negative feedback, and it is essential that the amplifier operate in a stable manner. In other words, the feedback must be negative over the entire frequency range of the amplifier. All amplifier configurations have a nonlinear phase characteristic, and the phase shift is greatest near the high-frequency limit of an op amp. It is evident that if the phase shift is excessive at a frequency for which the amplifier gain is greater than unity, a negative-feedback loop can function as a positive-feedback loop and cause the amplifier to oscillate at that frequency. Figure 7–17 exemplifies the frequency and phase response of a conventional RC-coupled amplifier. Note that the phase shift is leading at low frequencies, and lagging at high frequencies. Low-frequency lead is caused by the series coupling capacitors. High-frequency lag is caused by the stray and distributed shunt capacitances in the amplifier. If a direct-coupled amplifier is employed (such as an op amp), there is zero phase shift at low frequencies; however, the high-frequency phase shift is the same as in an ac-coupled amplifier.

If an amplifier has a sharp high-frequency cutoff (rapid roll-off), its phase characteristic changes more rapidly, or, its phase characteristic becomes more nonlinear. Since there is a definite relation between

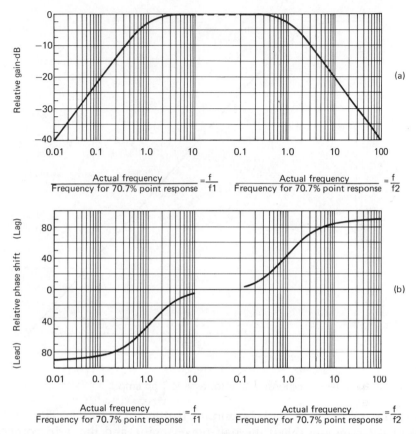

Fig. 7–17 Characteristics of a simple RC-coupled amplifier. **(a)** Frequency response curve; **(b)** Phase response curve.

the frequency response and the phase response of an amplifier, it follows that its frequency characteristic shows whether the amplifier will be stable or unstable under conditions of negative-feedback operation. This criterion of amplifier stability is called a Bode plot or a Bode diagram. With reference to Figure 7–17(a), observe that the frequency response curve shows dB gain versus frequency. Note also that in the frequency interval from 10 to 100, the gain decreases 20 dB, or 20 dB per decade. This rate of decrease is the same as 6.4 dB per octave. An octave means a doubling in frequency, such as 10 to 20, 20 to 40, 40 to 80, and so on. We will now consider how the attenuation in dB per octave is related to op-amp stability. This criterion can also be stated as the permissible attenuation in dB per decade (a frequency change of 10 to 1).

With reference to Figure 7–18, a frequency response curve is shown for a typical op amp. This curve indicates a maximum gain of 100 dB,

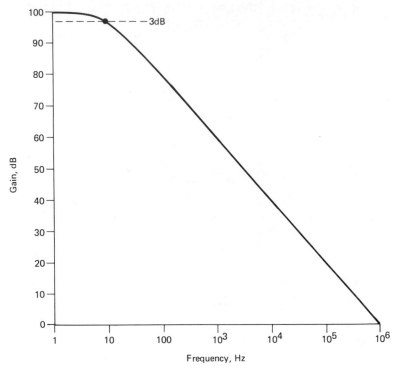

Fig. 7–18 Frequency response curve for a typical op amp.

with the −3 dB point at 10 Hz, and the 0 dB point at 1 MHz. The −3 dB point is commonly called the half-power point, and the 0 dB point is called the unity gain bandwidth. To make a Bode plot of this frequency characteristic, a straight-line approximation is drawn, as shown in Figure 7–19. Two break points are located. The first break point occurs at full gain and at the −3 dB frequency. The second break point occurs at the unity-gain (0 dB) frequency. A straight line is drawn to connect the break points. The slope of this line is then noted. In this example, the gain decreases 100 dB in five decades, or 20 dB in one decade, or 6 dB per octave. Note carefully that the rule for op-amp stability when negative feedback is used stipulates:

> *The attenuation slope of the Bode plot*
> *must not exceed 40 dB per decade.*

It follows that the Bode plot depicted in Figure 7–19 represents a stable op-amp frequency characteristic. Many op amps are designed to have an attenuation slope of approximately 20 dB per decade. Or, an op amp that is designed with an excessively steep attenuation slope will have terminals available to which networks can be connected to modify

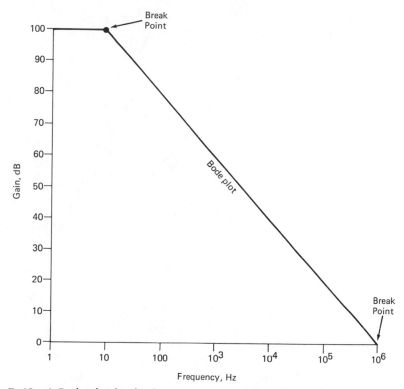

Fig. 7–19 A Bode plot for the frequency characteristic depicted in Fig. 7–18.

the attenuation slope. Some op amps are designed with attenuation slopes of nearly 40 dB per decade. Figure 7–20 shows comparative Bode plots of 20 dB per decade and 40 dB per decade. With all other things being equal, an op amp with a steeper attenuation slope will have a greater power bandwidth or full-power frequency response, as exemplified in Figure 7–21. Thus, using a negative-feedback loop that provides a 30 dB gain with respect to a 100 dB open-loop gain, a Bode-plot slope of 20 dB per decade provides a power bandwidth of 30 kHz, whereas a Bode-plot slope of 40 dB per decade provides a power bandwidth of 180 kHz. In other words, a six-fold increase in power bandwidth is provided in this particular example, simply by increasing the attenuation slope from 20 dB per decade to 40 dB per decade.

7.8 AVOIDANCE OF DAMAGE TO OP AMPS

Previous mention was made of the susceptibility of op amps to heat damage. This danger occurs during soldering operations, and can also occur if the op amp is made to function under overcurrent condi-

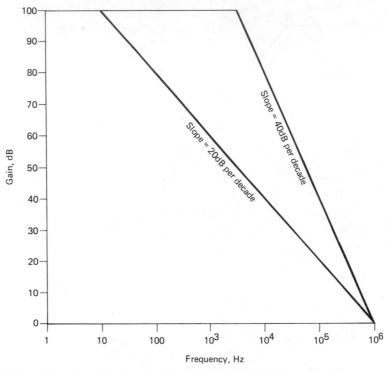

Fig. 7–20   Bode plots showing slopes of 20 dB and 40 dB per decade.

tions. Damage commonly results from excessive power-supply voltage, accidental reversal of power-supply polarity, input-stage overloading, and output-stage overloading. Excessive power-supply voltage causes breakdown of IC transistor collector-base junctions. Although breakdown may not be destructive in itself, an overcurrent condition arises which may burn out the transistor or melt the thin leads. Again, excessive input voltage may break down base-emitter junctions in the input stage. In case an overcurrent situation occurs, the affected transistor(s) can be burned out. Damage can be caused by reversal of power-supply polarity owing to overcurrent flow through junctions that are normally reverse-biased. Finally, damage can be caused by output-stage overloading owing to excessive heat dissipation. In other words, an op amp may be destroyed if its output terminal is accidentally short-circuited to ground, for example.

REVIEW QUESTIONS

1. What is the difference between pulse-amplitude modulation and other types of time-division multiplexing?

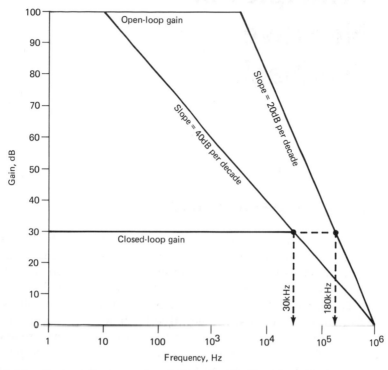

Fig. 7–21 Comparative power bandwidths for 20 dB and 40 dB slopes.

2. In reference to Fig. 7–4, how would the three output waveforms be displayed one above the other on an oscilloscope?

3. What is an analog computer?

4. How does a chopper-stabilized amplifier function?

5. What is a varactor diode?

6. What advantage does a varactor chopper have over other chopper arrangements?

7. In an amplifier, is the phase shift leading or lagging at high frequencies?

8. What is the rule for op amp stability when negative feedback is used?

9. What is the relationship between the Bode-plot slope and the power bandwidth of an op amp?

10. What are some of the possible causes for op amp failure?

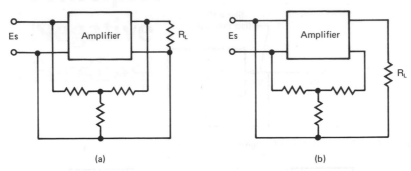

Fig. 8–4   Other basic negative-feedback arrangements. **(a)** Voltage feedback, parallel connection to amplifier input; **(b)** Current feedback, parallel connection to amplifier input.

foregoing examples serve to illustrate the fact that a negative-feedback arrangement can be chosen which will increase the input impedance and increase the output impedance of an amplifier, or, will decrease the input impedance and decrease the output impedance, or, will increase the input impedance and decrease the output impedance, or, will decrease the input impedance and increase the output impedance. Note that the arrangement in Figure 8–2 is called a series-parallel (SP) configuration; the arrangement in Figure 8–3 is called a series-series (SS) configuration; the arrangement in Figure 8–4(a) is called a parallel-parallel (PP) configuration; the arrangement in Figure 8–4(b) is called a parallel-series (PS) configuration.

8.2   BASIC NEGATIVE-FEEDBACK ANALYSIS

Referring to Figure 8–5, an amplifier that has an open-loop voltage gain of A times develops a voltage E_o across its load in response to an input voltage E_i. Note that a portion of the output voltage E_o from across the load R_L is fed back in series with the input source voltage E_s. A fraction, β, of the output voltage is fed back in opposing phase to E_s. Therefore, E_i is equal to the difference between these two terms, as given by the equation:

$$E_i = E_s - \beta E_o \qquad (8\text{–}1)$$

Note that E_o and E_i are related by the equation:

$$E_o = AE_i \qquad (8\text{–}2)$$

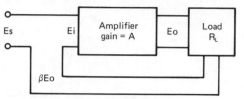

Fig. 8–5 Feedback amplifier arrangement for analysis.

In turn, the system amplification with negative feedback is written:

$$\frac{E_o}{E_s} = A_s = \frac{E_o}{E_s - \beta E_o} \qquad (8\text{–}3)$$

Since a resistive load is indicated in Figure 8–5, βE_o is the same whether voltage-feedback or current-feedback is utilized. Conversely, if the load is an impedance, βE_o will have both a real (resistive) component and an imaginary (reactive) component, and the load-voltage waveform will be different from the load-current waveform. As an illustration, Figure 8–6 shows an impedance load comprising a 0.01 μF capacitor and a 10 k resistor. The load voltage consists of a 1-kHz sine wave with a 3-kHz harmonic, and the voltage waveform has a single peak. On the other hand, the load current has a double peak, although it also consists of a 1-kHz sine wave and a 3-kHz harmonic. This change is caused by phase shift in the load; the third-harmonic current also has a relatively greater amplitude than the third-harmonic voltage. Therefore, analysis of negative feedback with impedance loads is comparatively involved.

Note that the T pads depicted in Figures 8–2, 8–3, and 8–4 may be resistive, or they may have reactive components. In the latter case, the feedback signal βE_o will not have the same waveform as E_o. Wave filters sometimes employ multiloop feedback, and a combination of voltage feedback and current feedback may be utilized. This combination is called bridge feedback. At this point, it is helpful to consider the equivalent circuit for an op amp (OVA), inasmuch as the schematic diagram for an op amp with negative feedback is simplified in equivalent-circuit form. While referring to Figure 8–7, recall that the open-loop and closed-loop gains of the system are given by the equations:

$$\text{Open-loop Gain} = \frac{V_o}{V_i} \qquad (8\text{–}4)$$

$$\text{Closed-loop Gain} = \frac{V_o}{V_s} \qquad (8\text{–}5)$$

As noted previously, these are approximate equations, but are suf-

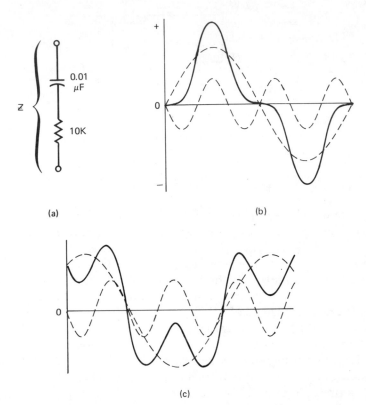

(a) (b)

(c)

Fig. 8–6 Example of differing voltage and current waveforms. **(a)** Impedance load;
(b) Voltage across the impedance; **(c)** Current through the impedance
(voltage across the resistor).

ficiently accurate to be considered as exact in most practical situations.
When a large amount of negative feedback is used, V_i becomes very
small, and may often be assumed to be zero for practical purposes. To
repeat an important point, when V_i is virtually zero, the input circuit
becomes equivalent to a simplified circuit in which the input component is connected to ground, instead of the op amp. Of course, the input
impedance of the amplifier is then virtually equal to the impedance of
the input component. Next, consider the relation between the input
current I_i and the feedback current I_f. When V_i is virtually zero, it follows that I_i and I_f are virtually equal and opposite. Or, expressed as an
equation:

$$I_f = -I_i \qquad\qquad (8\text{–}6)$$

In the equivalent circuit to be drawn for an op amp, it will be desirable to employ the variables V_s, I_i, and V_o. In other words, I_f will be

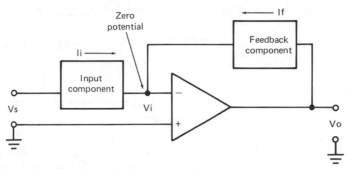

Fig. 8–7 Op-amp arrangement with negative feedback.

eliminated by substituting its negative equivalent $-I_i$. For purposes of substitution, it is helpful to change $-I_i$ to $+I_i$ by reversing the direction of I_i in the equivalent circuit. Then, we may analyze the arrangement in Figure 8–8 wherein I_f has been reversed in direction and its equal variable I_i substituted. Observe that since the inverting input of the op amp is at virtually zero potential, we may consider that the feedback component is connected to ground instead of to the op amp. When these circuit-action principles are combined, they may be expressed as the equivalent circuit for an op amp depicted in Figure 8–9. This equivalent circuit has the advantage that it shows almost at a glance how the system behavior will be changed by variation of the feedback-component characteristics. Note that this equivalent circuit has been derived for a parallel-parallel (PP) configuration.

It is instructive to observe how the equivalent circuit shown in Figure 8–9 applies to the analysis of an op-amp integrating circuit. Figure 8–10 shows a basic integrator configuration and its equivalent circuit. Assume that a step-function voltage is applied to the input terminals of the equivalent circuit. In turn, a constant current I_i is drawn by the input circuit. This input circuit is isolated from the output circuit. The value of I_i is equal to E_s/R, where E_s is the value of the step-function voltage. Next, the constant current I_i flows in the output circuit and charges C to produce a linear ramp waveform. The output voltage is dropped across C; if a load resistor R_L is utilized, the output voltage is dropped across C and R_L operating as an output voltage divider. The effect of R_L is to reduce the output voltage without changing the ramp waveform. Note that if R_L has zero resistance, there will be zero output voltage.

Next, consider how the equivalent circuit depicted in Figure 8–9 applies to the analysis of an op-amp differentiating circuit. Figure 8–11 shows a basic differentiator configuration and its equivalent circuit. Assume that a step-function voltage is applied to the input terminals of the equivalent circuit. In turn, an impulse current I_i is drawn by capaci-

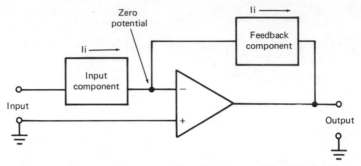

Fig. 8–8 Op-amp arrangement revised for obtaining an equivalent circuit.

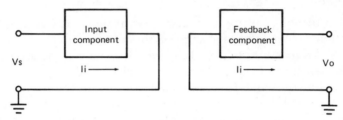

Fig. 8–9 Equivalent circuit corresponding to Fig. 8–8.

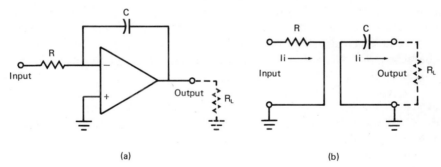

          (a)   (b)

Fig. 8–10 Op-amp integrator arrangement. **(a)** Configuration; **(b)** Equivalent circuit.

tor C. Next, this same impulse current flows in the output circuit and produces an I_iR voltage drop across R. The output voltage is dropped across R. If a load resistor R_L is utilized, the output voltage is reduced, because the effective value of R is reduced by R_L operating as an output voltage divider. Note that if R_L has zero resistance, there will be zero output voltage. From a practical viewpoint, there is a limit to the voltage that can be dropped across R in Figure 8–11, just as there is a limit to the voltage that can build up across C in Figure 8–10. This limit is determined by the supply voltage for the op amp.

    With reference to Figure 8–10(b), observe that the input impedance

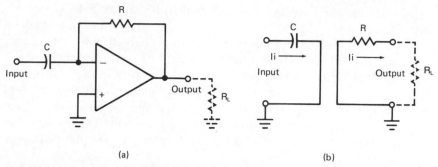

Fig. 8–11 Op-amp differentiator arrangement. **(a)** Configuration; **(b)** Equivalent circuit.

of an op-amp integrator is purely resistive, and that the output impedance is purely capacitive. Next, with reference to Figure 8–11(b), observe that the input impedance of an op-amp differentiator is purely capacitive, and that the output impedance is purely resistive. Consider the voltage gains provided by these configurations. With reference to Figure 8–10(a), the gain of the integrator arrangement is evidently equal to the quotient of X_C and R. Thus, the voltage gain is given by the equation:

$$\text{Gain} = \frac{\dfrac{1}{j2\pi fC}}{R} \tag{8–7}$$

This equation states that the input current and the feedback current are 90° out of phase with each other, as indicated by the j term. The equation also states that the gain is not constant, but is inversely proportional to frequency. Thus, this is a simple example of the fact that analysis of op-amp response with a reactive negative-feedback loop is comparatively involved. However, it is evident from the general form of Equation (8–7) that when the frequency is very low, the gain will be very high, inasmuch as the reactance of C will be very high and very little negative feedback will occur. On the other hand, when the frequency is very high, the gain will be very low, inasmuch as the reactance of C will be very small, and a very large amount of negative feedback will occur.

Next, referring to Figure 8–11(a), the gain of the differentiator arrangement is evidently equal to the quotient of R and X_C. Thus, the voltage gain is given by the equation:

$$\text{Gain} = \frac{R}{\dfrac{1}{j2\pi fC}} \tag{8–8}$$

Note that the j reference is different in Equation (8–8), compared with Equation (8–7). In other words, the j term in Equation (8–8) does not involve the feedback loop of the op amp. Instead, the j term states that there is a 90° phase difference between the driving voltage and the input current. There is no phase shift in the feedback loop. Nevertheless, the gain analysis remains comparatively involved. It is evident from the general form of Equation (8–8) that the gain is directly proportional to frequency, and that when the frequency is very low, the gain will be very low. On the other hand, when the frequency is very high, the gain will be very high.

8.3 EQUIVALENT CIRCUIT FOR
OP-AMP LOW-PASS FILTER

It is instructive to observe the equivalent circuit for the basic low-pass filter arrangement shown in Figure 8–12. Note that the output portion of the equivalent circuit is the same as that for an op-amp integrator, and that the input portion comprises a T-section low-pass RC filter with its output terminal connected to ground. This T section has the same

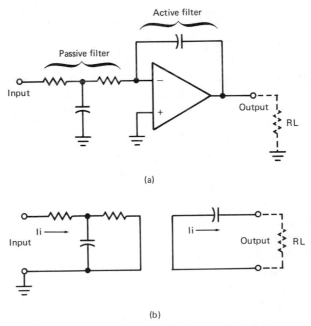

Fig. 8–12 Basic low-pass op-amp filter arrangement. **(a)** Configuration; **(b)** Equivalent circuit.

frequency response as an L section, and is functionally a loaded L section. Loading of an L section reduces the output voltage without changing its frequency response. In turn, the frequency characteristic of the T section is given by the universal frequency-response chart depicted in Figure 8–13. Effectively the T section and the op-amp integrator are cascaded. In turn, the output from the first low-pass filter is multiplied by the output from the second low-pass filter. The result is to produce a sharper filter cutoff characteristic than can be provided by the passive filter alone, or by the active filter alone. As an illustration, Figure 8–14 shows how the cutoff characteristic is sharpened when two identical low-pass sections are operated in cascade.

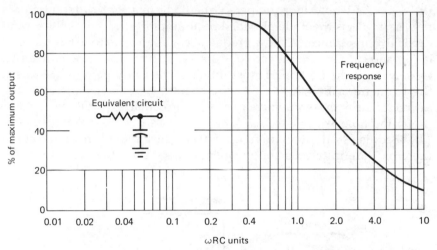

Fig. 8–13 Universal RC frequency-response chart for an L-section low-pass filter.

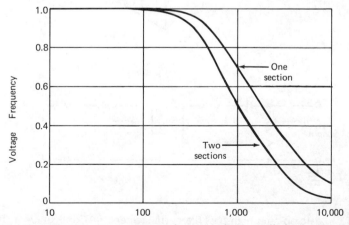

Fig. 8–14 Comparative one-section and two-section cutoff characteristics.

8.4 EQUIVALENT CIRCUIT FOR
OP-AMP HIGH-PASS FILTER

A basic op-amp high-pass filter arrangement and its equivalent circuit are shown in Figure 8–15. This configuration comprises a passive RC filter section and an amplifier. In turn, the frequency characteristic is determined by the RC section, and the op amp merely steps up the output amplitude from the filter. Note that the series resistor R_s is included to limit the gain at high frequencies. This is a practical requirement for system stability. To understand this requirement, consider the basic differentiator arrangement and its Bode plot, pictured in Figure 8–16. As would be anticipated, the Bode plot for a differentiator is not as simple as the Bode plot for a basic amplifier, because of the input capacitive reactance. At low frequencies, the capacitive reactance is large, and at zero frequency (dc) the capacitive reactance is infinite. Observe that the Bode plot must intersect the unity-gain (0 dB) axis at the frequency where $X_C = R$. As the operating frequency increases, X_C decreases and the gain increases at approximately 6 dB per octave. (Refer to Table 8–1).

Because of limitations in op-amp characteristics, the gain cannot increase indefinitely as the frequency increases. However, since the

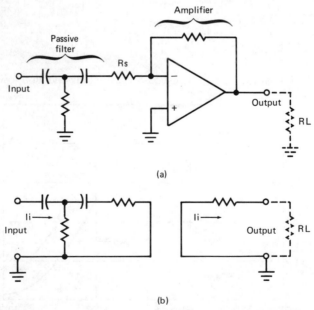

(a)

(b)

Fig. 8–15   Basic op-amp high-pass filter arrangement. **(a)** Configuration; **(b)** Equivalent circuit.

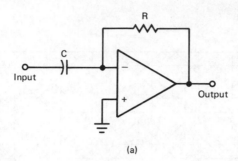

(a)

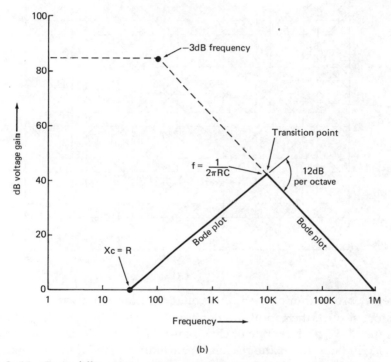

(b)

Fig. 8–16 Basic differentiator arrangement. **(a)** Configuration; **(b)** Bode plot.

configuration has maximum gain at its highest response frequency, random noise is a serious problem in the basic arrangement. Therefore, it is desirable to limit the gain more or less at the high-frequency end. Even more serious from a practical viewpoint is that the rate of closure on the Bode plot is approximately 12 dB per octave, as indicated in Figure 8–16. In turn, the op amp is unstable in the basic configuration, and it is necessary to employ some means of reducing the rate of closure. One useful method is to insert an input "stop" resistor, as depicted in Figure 8–17. As the operating frequency is increased, X_C decreases, and

TABLE 8–1

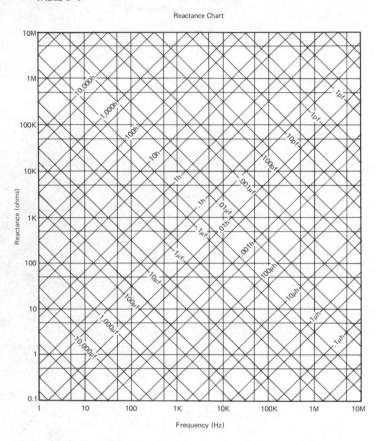

Reactance Chart

a greater proportion of the input voltage is dropped across the "stop" resistor. In turn, the top of the Bode plot becomes truncated, as shown in Figure 8–17, and the rate of closure is reduced to within stable limits. To recapitulate, this is the reason for including R_s in Figure 8–15(a).

Next, observe that the high-frequency gain of a basic differentiator can also be reduced by employing a capacitor in shunt to the negative-feedback resistor, as shown in Figure 8–18. This is called a "stop" capacitor. Thus, the configuration utilizes a "double stop". The chief advantage of a "double stop" is improved noise rejection. On the other hand, high-frequency gain is further reduced, so that differentiating action is proportionally degraded. Because one slope change occurs with respect to the input circuit, and the other slope change occurs with respect to the negative-feedback circuit, the rate of closure in Figure 8–18(b) is actually 6 dB, and not 12 dB per octave, as would appear at first glance.

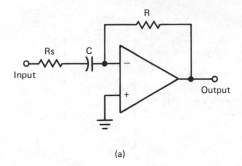

(a)

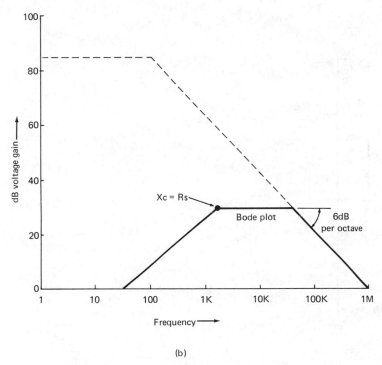

(b)

Fig. 8–17 Basic differentiator arrangement with "stop" resistor. **(a)** Configuration; **(b)** Bode plot.

8.5 BODE PLOT FOR OP-AMP INTEGRATOR

At this point, it is instructive to consider the Bode plot for a basic op-amp integrator; the plot is very informative in evaluating the low-pass characteristics of low-pass filter action. With reference to Figure 8–19, a Bode plot is first drawn for the op amp alone, as depicted by the dotted lines. Then, the frequency is calculated at which the reactance of

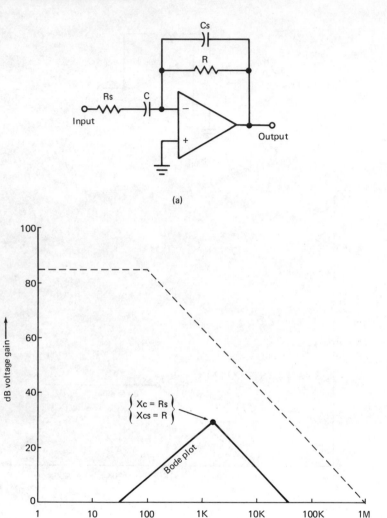

(a)

(b)

Fig. 8–18 Basic differentiator with "double stop". **(a)** Configuration; **(b)** Bode plot.

the negative-feedback capacitor is equal to the input resistance. A line is then drawn through this frequency, parallel with the first Bode plot line. The second Bode plot line defines the frequency response of the integrator configuration. Note that the low-frequency gain is limited only by the capability of the op amp. Therefore, operating difficulties will arise in practice. As an illustration, any small dc offset voltage would

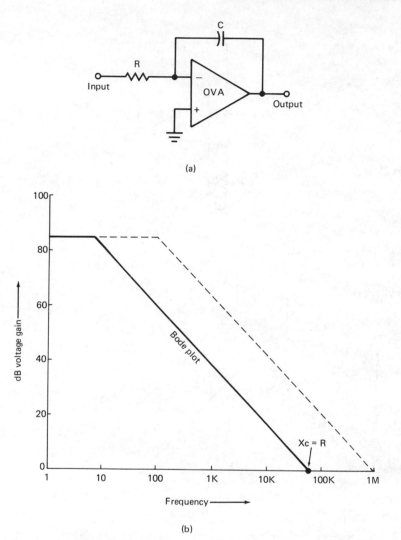

(a)

(b)

Fig. 8–19 Bode plot for the basic op-amp differentiator. **(a)** Configuration; **(b)** Construction of plot.

be integrated by the configuration depicted in Figure 8–19, and the integrator would ramp up or down until it went into saturation. Moreover, if there is a residual charge on the negative-feedback capacitor when the op amp is turned on, a heavy current could flow that would destroy the op amp. The solution to both difficulties is to shunt the negative-feedback capacitor with a resistor, as depicted in Figure 8–20.

Observe in Figure 8–20 that R_s operates as a negative-feedback stabilizing resistor, and R_o operates as an offset-voltage balancing re-

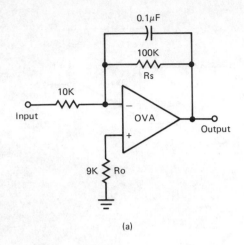

(a)

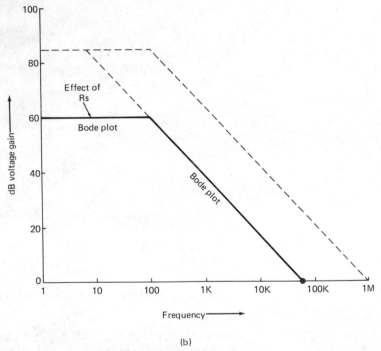

(b)

Fig. 8–20 Practical op-amp integrator with negative-feedback stabilizing resistor. (a) Configuration; (b) Bode plot.

sistor, as explained previously. Another stabilization factor in any op-amp arrangement that employs negative feedback is the effect of capacitive loading across the output terminals. Thus far, we have considered resistive loading only. When a resistive load is shunted by capacitance, the load voltage becomes shifted in phase, and this phase shift is a function of frequency. Since the negative-feedback voltage source is the load voltage, the negative-feedback characteristic then becomes a function of frequency, and high-frequency peaking occurs as depicted in Figure 8–21. In turn, the slope of the open-loop response is increased, and if the rate of closure approaches 12 dB per octave, the system may break into oscillation. Therefore, the output load for an op amp must not have a capacitive component sufficiently large that system operation is disturbed.

8.6 OP-AMP OUTPUT IMPEDANCE AND PP NEGATIVE FEEDBACK

Op amps are rated for open-loop output impedance, ranging from approximately 3 ohms to 1000 ohms. Most op amps have an open-loop output impedance in the vicinity of 150 ohms. However, when negative feedback is employed, the effective output impedance of the op amp becomes considerably less, and in most applications the effective output impedance will be less than one ohm. The lowest effective output impedance is obtained when maximum negative feedback is used. Thus, the voltage-follower configuration provides the lowest output impedance. With reference to the voltage-follower arrangement shown in Figure 8–22, the effective output impedance may be determined as follows. Suppose that the load demand is increased by a small amount ΔI_L. In turn, the amplifier output voltage e_o must increase by a small amount $\Delta I_L Z_{out}$, where Z_{out} is the rated open-loop output impedance of the op amp. This change in output voltage corresponds to a change of input voltage between the op-amp input terminals given by the equation:

$$\Delta E_i = \frac{-\Delta e_o}{A} \tag{8–9}$$

where A is the open-loop gain of the op amp.

With reference to Figure 8–22, since the output terminal is connected to the inverting-input terminal of the op amp, it follows that E_o must decrease by Δe_i. In turn, the effective output impedance is given by the equation:

$$Z_{eoi} = \frac{\Delta E_o}{\Delta I_L} = \frac{\Delta E_o}{A} \cdot \frac{Z_{out}}{\Delta e_o} = \frac{Z_{out}}{A} \tag{8–10}$$

As an illustration of the application of Equation (8–10), if the op amp is rated for an open-loop output impedance of 150 ohms, and an

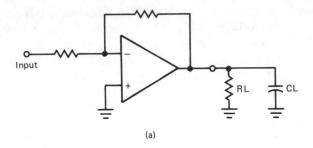

(a)

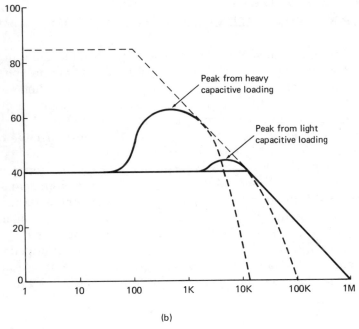

(b)

Fig. 8–21 Effect of capacitive loading across op-amp output terminals. **(a)** Basic negative-feedback configuration; **(b)** Bode plot modification produced by capacitive loading.

open-loop gain of 20,000, its effective output impedance will be 0.0075 ohms in the voltage-follower configuration.

8.7 CONSTANT GAIN-BANDWIDTH PRODUCT

The gain-bandwidth product of an op-amp was previously defined as the frequency at which the open-loop gain is equal to unity, or 0 dB. As an illustration, the gain-bandwidth product depicted by

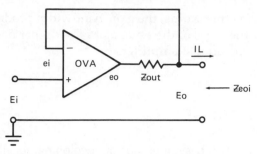

Fig. 8–22 Op-amp output impedance is decreased by PP negative feedback.

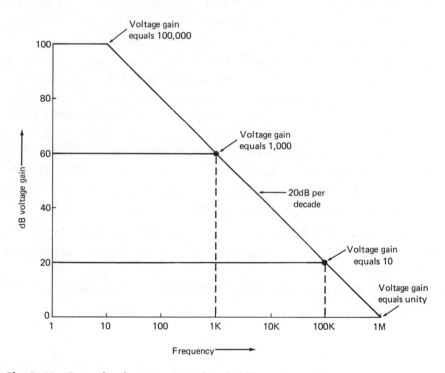

Fig. 8–23 Example of constant gain-bandwidth product (10^6).

the Bode plot in Figure 8–23 is 10^6. Next, observe that the gain-band-width product of an op amp may be a constant for any value of full-power closed-loop gain. The gain-bandwidth product will be constant if the slope of the Bode plot is 20 dB per decade, as exemplified in Figure 8–23. Two values of negative feedback are depicted, which reduce the open-loop gain to 60 dB and 20 dB, respectively. At 60 dB gain, the full-power bandwidth is 1 kHz, and the corresponding product of voltage gain and frequency is 10^6. Next, at 20 dB gain, the full-power bandwidth is 100 kHz, and the corresponding product of voltage gain and frequency is 10^6. In other words, the gain-bandwidth product is a constant, provided that the slope of the Bode plot is 20 dB per decade, as is often the case with operational amplifiers.

REVIEW QUESTIONS

1. What are the two basic methods of developing negative feedback?
2. How is voltage feedback developed?
3. What are the effects of voltage feedback?
4. What are the effects of current feedback?
5. Draw a diagram of each of the following circuits for feedback in an op amp: series-parallel, series-series, parallel-parallel, and parallel-series.
6. What is the gain of an op amp when the output voltage with output feedback is 1 mV, the input voltage is 10 μV and the feedback factor is .01?
7. What is the form of the input and output impedances of an integrator?
8. What is the form of the input and output impedances of a differentiator?
9. What is the effect when two low-pass filters are operated in cascade?
10. What is the reason for resistor R_s in Fig. 8–15(a)?
11. What is the advantage of the "double stop" arrangement in Fig. 8–18?
12. What is the effect of excessive capacitive load across the output of an op amp employing negative feedback?
13. What is the typical open-loop output impedance of an op amp?
14. Which circuit configuration gives the lowest output impedance?

ANSWERS TO REVIEW QUESTIONS

CHAPTER 1

1. differential

2. offset

3. special case of noninverting amplifier in which the gain is unity

4. Common mode—signal voltages are cancelled out.

5. by use of external phase-shift compensating networks

6. an overdriven amplifier

7. It causes a much sharper cutoff frequency characteristic.

8. V_s is the input signal
   V_o is the output signal
   V_o/V_i = open loop gain
   V_o/V_s = closed loop gain
   f_c = cutoff frequency

9. 159 Hz

10. (a) no insertion loss
    (b) op amp acts as a buffer
    (c) lower output Z

11. 100 kHz

12. a state-variable filter

13. Its frequency and selectivity can be adjusted and it provides a very sharp cutoff characteristic.

14. 159 kHz

15. Capacitors fail more often than resistors.

16. leaky capacitors, resistors off value, low ac voltages, cold solder joints, cracked circuit board and defective op amp

CHAPTER 2

1. linear—the output varies directly with input
   nonlinear—the output does not vary directly with input
2. constant current sink
3. input R = 10k ohms
   output R = 10 ohms
4. Offset is no problem when negative feedback is not used.
5. The voltages must be the same polarity; with ac the inputs must have the same frequency and phase.
6. The frequency must not exceed the rated frequency of the op amp.
7. 101
8. practically equal to R_i
9. less than one megohm to several hundred megohms
10. R_o of the circuit will be less than the output R of the op amp itself.
11. the power supply
12. When the inverting amplifier goes into saturation, supplying negative feedback that acts as positive feedback to hold the input stage in saturation.
13. An excessive offset voltage is developed.
14. The op amp has greater gain than a junction transistor.
15. an amplifier that amplifies the difference between two signals
16. 2 millivolts
17. to prevent circuit loading
18. to prevent turning on the junctions of the op amp, thereby giving a low reading
19. the maximum rate of change to an input signal that suddenly changes from a maximum positive value to a maximum negative value

CHAPTER 3

1. the voltage induced in an inductor that opposes any change of current in the inductor
2. Current lags the voltage by 90°.
3. Current leads the voltage by 90°.

4. a network for simulation of inductance

5. oscillations

6. 10,000 Henrys

7. one that has two inputs and one output

8. in high-pass active filters

9. in low-pass active filters

10. Less current flows as the voltage is increased.

11. 200 μF

12. (a) open-loop DC voltage gain
    (b) open-loop gain stability versus temperature
    (c) open-loop gain stability versus supply voltage
    (d) open-loop input Z
    (e) open-loop output Z
    (f) maximum output capacity
    (g) open-loop bandwidth

CHAPTER 4

1. to act as an amplifier; to act as an integrator

2. as a current-balancing circuit to prevent an output due to input offset current

3. a current differencing input stage to cause a balancing current

4. diode D11

5. a current-operated device

6. used in fuel injectors, anti-skid controls, and speed controls

7. See Fig. 4–17.

8. .5 μvolts

9. See Fig. 4–17.

10. (a) input offset voltage (see formula 4–2)
    (b) input voltage versus drift temperature (see formula 4–3)
    (c) input voltage drift versus supply (see formula 4–4)
    (d) input voltage drift versus time (see formula 4–5)
    (e) input noise (see formula 4–6)
    (f) input current offset (see formula 4–7)
    (g) input current drift versus temperature (see formula 4–8)
    (h) input current drift versus supply (see formula 4–9)

CHAPTER 5

1. frequency selection
2. 10 kHz
3. positive feedback and phase
4. the thermal lag of the bulb
5. 12.98 kHz
6. 1 kHz
7. the op amp slew rate
8. the time constant of R3C1
9. the slew rate of the op amp
10. 0.5 volt per microsecond
11. $\text{drift} = \dfrac{\Delta V_{out}}{10 \text{ meg}}$
12. −3 dB
13. see Fig. 5–20 or 5–21
14. 8.66μsec
15. the op amp is loaded with a capacitor decade box until unstable operation occurs.
16. $Z_{in} = 9R_s$
17. see Fig. 5–22.

CHAPTER 6

1. 1,000 or 60 dB voltage gain
2. the gain increases steadily.
3. greater negative feedback, greater bandwidth
4. decreases the bandwidth
5. 100 mW to 750 mW
6. to prevent a peak at around 4.5 MHz
7. stray capacitance in the structure of the op amp
8. $\dfrac{V_{out}}{V_{in}} = \dfrac{-Z_f}{Z_r}$

9. a circuit that combines and amplifies two or more input signals

10. reducing the signals to a specified fraction of their original value

11. The 30-volt supply voltage adds to both the inverting-output and the noninverting-output section.

12. as an agc amplifier

13. increase the input Z

14. PNP has poorer frequency response.

15. Don't bend the leads too tight and don't overheat when soldering.

CHAPTER 7

1. PAM is analog and others are digital.

2. by adding dc voltages of different values

3. an electronic model of a mathematical model

4. The dc signal is chopped to develop pulses that are proportional to the dc signal, which can then be operated on as if it were an ac signal. This limits dc drift.

5. a reverse biased diode that operates as a voltage controlled capacitor

6. less flicker noise

7. lagging

8. The attenuation slope of the Bode-plot must not exceed 40 dB per decade.

9. Decreasing the attenuation slope decreases the power bandwidth factor.

10. excess heat, power supply polarity reversal, excessive supply voltage, shorted output, output stage overloading and input stage overloading

CHAPTER 8

1. current feedback and voltage feedback

2. Voltage drop across part of the load impedance is inserted in series with the input-signal voltage.

3. decreased gain, increased bandwidth, decreased output Z and decreased or increased input Z.

4. decreased gain, increased bandwidth, increased output Z, and increased input Z.

5. See Fig. 8-2, 8-3, 8-4a and 8-4b respectively.

6. A = 50. Note that beta is negative.

7. input purely capacitive and output purely resistive

8. input resistive and output purely capacitive

9. a sharper cutoff characteristic

10. R_s is a stop resistor used to provide stability to the circuit.

11. to provide stability and improve noise rejection

12. oscillation

13. 150 ohms

14. a voltage follower

REFERENCE
MATTER

APPENDIX A

Low-Power Triple Operational Amplifier Integrated Circuit

FOR INVERTING AMPLIFIERS, VOLTAGE COMPARATORS, LOW-DRIFT SAMPLE-AND-HOLD CIRCUITS, ACTIVE FILTERS, BATTERY-POWERED CIRCUITS

- External Control of Supply Current and Output Drive
- Operation with ±1.5 V to ±15 V Power Supplies
- 80 dB Gain with 20 kΩ Load
- ±30 V Differential Input Voltage Range
- Drives Large Capacitive Loads (>1,000 pF)
- Internally–Compensated
- Continuous Short–Circuit Protection
- Monolithic Construction
- Slew Rate 0.4 V/μsec Typical

The L144 is a monolithic low–power triple operational amplifier stabilized for all feedback configurations and capacitive loads by internal gain compensation. Low power requirements permit high voltage operation across the rated temperature range, as well as battery operation from ±1.5 V.

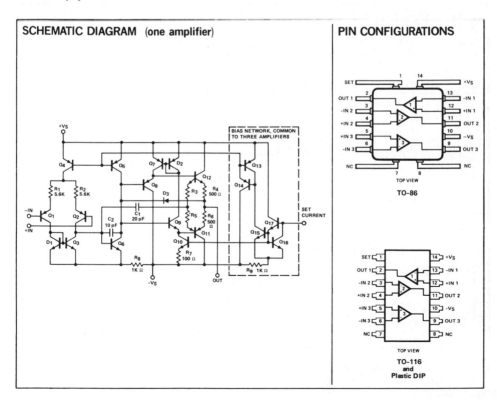

SCHEMATIC DIAGRAM (one amplifier)

PIN CONFIGURATIONS

. 179

ABSOLUTE MAXIMUM RATINGS

Supply Voltage .... ±18 V
Differential Input Voltage .... ±30 V
Input Voltage* (A Suffix) .... ±18 V
             (C Suffix) .... ±15 V
Output Shoft Circuit Duration**............. Indefinite
Operating Temperature Range.............. –55 to 125°C
Storage Temperature Range.............. –65 to 160°C
Lead Temperature (Soldering, 60 Sec) .... 300°C
Power Dissipation*** (TO-86) .... 750 mW
          (TO-116) .... 1,200 mW
         Plastic DIP .... 470 mW

* For supply voltages $< \pm 18$ V, maximum input voltage is equal to the supply voltage.

** Continuous short circuit is allowed for case temperatures to +125°C and ambient temperature to +70°C.

*** All leads welded or soldered to PC board. Derate 10 mW/°C for TO-86, 16 mW/°C for TO-116 above +70°C, and 6.3 mW/°C above 25°C for plastic DIP.

ELECTRICAL CHARACTERISTICS

All DC parameters are 100% tested at 25°C. Lots are sampled–tested for AC parameters, high and low temperature limits, to assure conformance with specifications.

				L144 A/B			L144C			Unit	Test Conditions (Unless Other–wise Noted) $V_S = \pm 15$ V, $R_L = 20$ kΩ, $R_{SET} = 3$ MΩ* Pin 1 to Pin 14
		Characteristic		-55°C/-25°C	25°C	125°C/85°C	0°C	25°C	70°C		
1	I N P U T	V_{OS} Input Offset Voltage	Max	6	5	6		10		mV	$R_S \leqslant 50$ KΩ
2			Typ		1		4	2	4		
3		I_{OS} Input Offset Current	Max		50			70		nA	
4			Typ		2			5			
5		I_{Bias} Input Bias Current	Max	200	200		250	250			
6			Typ		100			125			
7	O U T P U T	V_{OUT} Output Voltage Swing	Min		±10			±10		V	
8			Typ		±14						
9			Typ		±0.5			±0.4			$V_S = \pm 1.5$ V, $R_{SET} = 120$ KΩ
10		I_{SC} Output Short Circuit Current	Max		15					mA	$R_L = 0$
11			Typ		1.5						
12		A_{VOL} DC Voltage Gain	Typ	12	12	12	12	12	12	V/mV	
13			Min	3.0	3.0	3.0	1.0	1.0	1.0		
14	D Y N A M I C	S_r Slew Rate	Typ		0.4			0.4		V/μsec	
15											
16		Unity Gain Bandwidth	Typ		0.4			0.4		MHz	
17											
18		Crosstalk	Typ		-100			-100			f = 100 Hz
19		$CMRR$ Common Mode Rejection Ratio	Min		80			70		dB	$V_{IN} = \pm 12$ V
20			Typ		90			80			
21	S U P	$PSRR$ Power Supply Rejection Ratio	Min		80			80			
22			Typ		90			90			
23		I_S Supply Current	Max		350			400		μA	Unity Gain $V_{IN+} = 0$ on all amps

*I_{CC} is adjustable. See typical characteristics.

CMAC

TYPICAL CHARACTERISTICS

Open Loop Gain vs Frequency

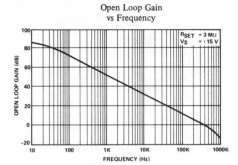

Gain Bandwidth Product vs Supply Current

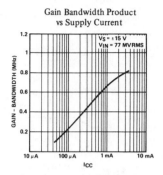

Slew Rate vs Supply Current

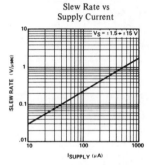

Open Loop Gain vs Temperature

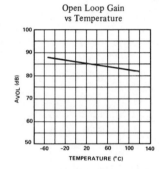

DC Open Loop Gain vs Supply Current

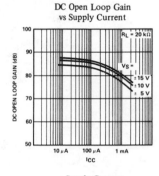

Supply Current vs Set Resistor and Supply Voltage

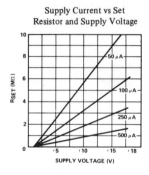

Input Bias Current vs Supply Current

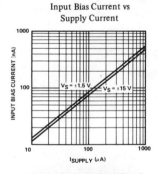

Supply Current vs Temperature

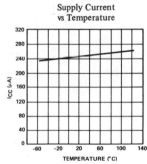

Voltage Follower Small Signal Pulse Response

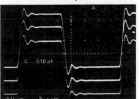

APPLICATIONS

Instrumentation Amplifier

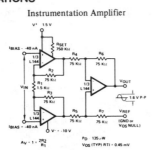

Active Filter

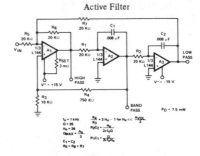

Precision Phase Splitter

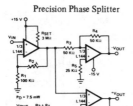

Double-Ended Limit Comparator

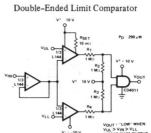

500 Hz Tone Detector

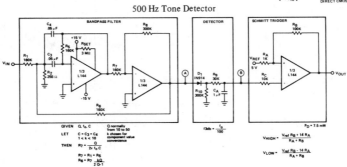

MECHANICAL DATA

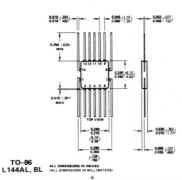

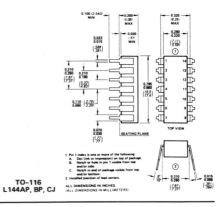

TO-86
L144AL, BL
ALL DIMENSIONS IN INCHES
(ALL DIMENSIONS IN MILLIMETERS)

TO-116
L144AP, BP, CJ
ALL DIMENSIONS IN INCHES
(ALL DIMENSIONS IN MILLIMETERS)

APPENDIX B

Micro-Power
Triple Op Amp

Marvin K. Vander Kooi

INTRODUCTION

The L144 is a monolithic triple operational amplifier circuit with an external programming feature for power dissipation and input bias current control. It finds application in RC active filters, instrumentation amplifiers, micro–power comparators, and numerous general signal processing circuits. The L144 is a practical industry standard op amp wherever low current drain, low voltage, low power, or very small physical size are the controlling criteria.

This Application Note describes the L144, how to program it, what the effects of slew rate limiting are, and some practical circuit applications.

The L144 has three operational amplifiers programmed by one external current setting resistor. It operates from power supplies ranging from ±18 V to as low as ±1.5 V with quiescent supply currents of from 10 μA to greater than 1 mA independent of supply voltage. The schematic shown in Figure 1 reveals a general–purpose PNP input transistor op amp with an outstanding difference. The master bias current is not set by an internal resistor strung from V^+ to V^-, but is brought out to an external pin. This allows the user to determine the operating currents of each stage through a system of current mirrors. Of special interest to the designer are the equal collector currents of Q_1 and Q_2, which are derived from the output of Q_4. These collector currents, divided by a beta of approximately 50, determine the input bias currents for each amplifier. The ratio between the set current and the collector current of Q_4 is unity, which allows one to program the input bias current simply by changing the set current input of the device.

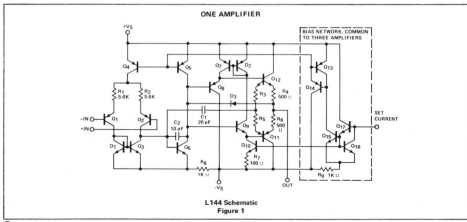

ONE AMPLIFIER

L144 Schematic
Figure 1

Input Bias Current and Supply Current

The relationship between supply current, supply voltage, and the setting resistor is shown in the graph and set current model of Figure 2. The two diodes of the set current model correspond to the base-emitter junctions of Q_{16} and Q_{17}.

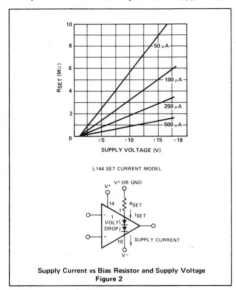

Supply Current vs Bias Resistor and Supply Voltage
Figure 2

Figure 3 shows the essentially linear relationship between input bias current and total quiescent supply current for the L144. The low input bias currents at low supply current levels allow the L144 to maintain good input specifications even with the large feedback and load resistor values normally encountered in micro-power applications.

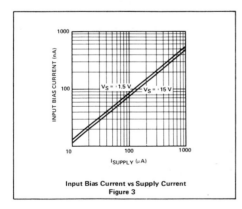

Input Bias Current vs Supply Current
Figure 3

The slightly lower input bias currents at the higher supply voltages are due to the narrower base width and higher beta encountered at $V_S = \pm 15$ V.

Frequency Response

At the data sheet standard supply current of 250 μA the typical Bode plot is as shown in Figure 4. The low fre—quency gain of approximately 85 dB rolls into a uniform -20-dB/decade slope until after the 0 dB unity gain crossing point. The variation of open loop gain with temperature is typically minus 3 dB per 100°C of temperature rise. The 400 kHz unity gain crossover gives a gain bandwidth pro-

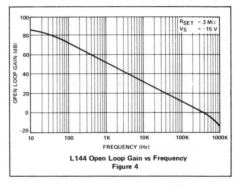

L144 Open Loop Gain vs Frequency
Figure 4

duct (GBWP) of 400,000. Figure 5 shows the variation of GBWP with supply current.

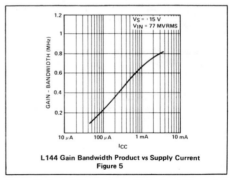

L144 Gain Bandwidth Product vs Supply Current
Figure 5

The vertical axis is linear whereas the horizontal I_{CC} axis is logarithmic, demonstrating that the GBWP does vary with I_{CC}, but at much less than the 1-to-1 ratio observed for other parameters.

Slew Rate

Slew rate is almost a direct function of supply current as shown in Figure 6. This follows from the fact that slew rate limiting is actually caused by the finite limits of the internal current sources (which charge and discharge the second stage compensation capacitor) varying with the externally-determined set current. An amplifier output changes from the small signal response shown on the Bode plot to a slew-rate-limited response when the rate of change of the output voltage exceeds the rate of change determined by slew rate limit of the amplifier. Since the maximum rate of

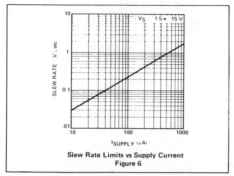

Slew Rate Limits vs Supply Current
Figure 6

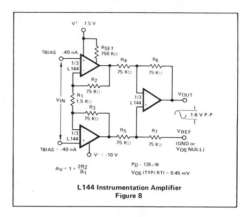

L144 Instrumentation Amplifier
Figure 8

change of a sine wave is a function of peak amplitude it is possible to trade maximum frequency for peak signal amplitude when operating at low power dissipation levels. Figure 7 shows the derivation[1] of an equation relating slew rate

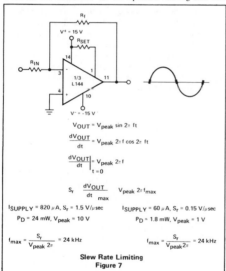

Slew Rate Limiting
Figure 7

S_r, sine wave amplitude V_{PEAK}, and frequency. The zero crossing of a sine wave is the point of maximum rate of change as shown after the derivative is taken and maximized. In both of the examples shown the maximum undistorted operating frequency is kept constant while juggling power dissipation, slew rate, and peak amplitude in an engineering tradeoff.

Instrumentation Amplifier

Figure 8 shows a single L144 chip used to construct a three-amplifier classical instrumentation amplifier. The entire circuit consumes only $135\mu W$ of power from a ±1.5 V power supply. With a gain of 101 the instrumentation amplifier is ideal in sensor interface and biomedical preamplifier applications.

The first stage provides all of the gain while the second stage is used to provide common mode rejection and double-ended to single-ended conversion. The resistor R_1 determines the gain of the circuit according to the equation:

$$A_V = 1 + \frac{2R_2}{R_1} \qquad (1)$$

The reference point at the base of R_7 can be used to determine the quiescent output voltage when there is no differential input voltage. This provides an easy single point to zero any net offset voltage (typically 0.45 mV referred to input) and/or to insert a trim resistor to improve common mode rejection ratio (CMRR). The CMRR depends heavily on the match between R_4/R_6 and R_5/R_7 and can be nulled if R_7 is broken into a resistor and a small-value trim potentiometer. Figure 9 shows the voltage gain and CMRR versus frequency for a typical instrumentation amplifier. The upper curve shows a calculated CMRR referred to input. The falloff and final rise in CMRR is due to the mismatch in gain rolloff between amplifiers in the first stage followed by a falloff in gain and consequent increase in rejection of the second stage.

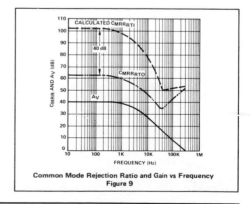

Common Mode Rejection Ratio and Gain vs Frequency
Figure 9

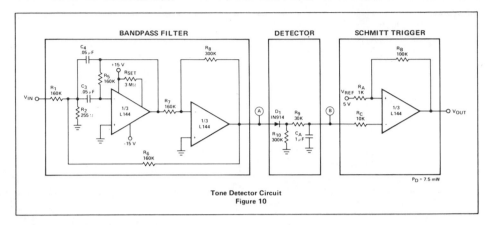

Tone Detector Circuit
Figure 10

Tone Detector

Another example of a single L144 providing the amplifiers for an entire system is shown in Figure 10. This tone detector circuit is made up of a two-amplifier multiple feedback bandpass filter followed by an AC–to–DC detector section and a Schmitt Trigger. The bandpass filter (with a Q of greater than 100) passes only 500 Hz inputs which are in turn rectified by D_1 and filtered by R_9 and C_A. This filtering action in combination with the trigger level of 5 V for the Schmitt device insures that at least 55 cycles of 500 Hz input must be present before the output will react to a tone input. The actual integrating capacitor waveform shown in Figure 11 was taken with a 1 volt peak 500 Hz sine wave input. The ratio between capacitor C_A charge and discharge is 1:11, due to resistors R_9 and R_{10}.

For frequencies other than the 500 Hz center frequency shown in the example the relevant bandpass filter[2] equations are:

GIVEN: Q, f_o, C (Q normally from 10 to 50)   (2)

LET: $C = C_3 = C_4$ (3)
         $1 \leqslant k \leqslant 10$ (k chosen for component value convenience)

THEN: $R_7 = \dfrac{Q}{2\pi f_o C}$ (4)

$$R_7 = R_1 = R_5 \qquad (5)$$

$$R_6 = R_7 \frac{kQ}{2Q - 1} \qquad (6)$$

$$R_2 = \frac{R_7}{Q^2 - 1 - \dfrac{2}{k} + \dfrac{1}{kQ}} \qquad (7)$$

$$R_8 = kR_7 \qquad (8)$$

$$H_0 = \sqrt{Q} \quad k \qquad (9)$$

In the example shown in Figure 10 the chosen value of k = 2 and the passive components used resulted in a measured Q (121) which was much greater than the expected 25. Reducing the value of R_8 caused the Q to decrease to the calculated value. (For lower component sensitivities use the 3-amplifier active filter shown in Figure 12). The center frequency of 498.4 Hz and H_0 of 9.226 were close to the calculated values of 500 Hz and 10.

The detector RC was designed to have a 3 dB down frequency of:

$$f_{3dB} = \frac{f_o}{100} \qquad (10)$$

while the Schmitt trigger operated around the reference voltage with trip points determined by:

$$V_{HIGH} = \frac{V_{REF} R_B + 14 R_A}{R_A + R_B} \qquad (11)$$

$$V_{LOW} = \frac{V_{REF} R_B - 14 R_A}{R_A + R_B} \qquad (12)$$

where ±14 V is the output swing with ±15 V supplies. The measured trip points agreed with the calculated values of 5.089 V and 4.81 V within 0.2 % in the circuit of Figure 10.

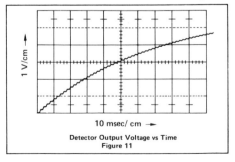

10 msec/ cm →

Detector Output Voltage vs Time
Figure 11

3 Amplifier Active Filter

The active filter shown in Figure 12 is a dual-integrator feedback resonator with band-pass, high-pass and low-pass outputs. It is a classical analog computer method of implementing a filter using three amplifiers and only two capacitors. With the L144 triple op amp it becomes cost-effective to use this configuration with its' attendant high Q values and low sensitivities.[3] The theoretical maximum value for Q is:

$$Q_{max} = \frac{A_{VOL}}{3} \tag{13}$$

where A_{VOL} is the open loop gain of amplifier A_1.

The controlling design equations are:

GIVEN: Q, f_o, & H_o (14)

LET: $R_5 = R_6 = R_7$ (Chosen for component (15)
$C_1 = C_2$ value convenience)

THEN: $\frac{R_4}{R_3} = 3 H_o - 1$ for $H_o \ll \frac{A_{VOL}}{3}$ (16)

$$R_2 C_2 = \frac{H_o}{2\pi f_o Q} \tag{17}$$

$$R_1 C_1 = \frac{Q}{2\pi f_o H_o} \tag{18}$$

The design example shown on Figure 12 was calculated as follows:

LET: Q = 26 (19)
f_o = 1 kHz
H_o = 26
$R_5 = R_6 = R_7$ = 20k
$C_1 = C_2$ = .008 μF
R_3 = 10k

THEN: $R_4 = (3H_o - 1) R_3 = 770k \approx 750k$ (20)

$$R_2 = \frac{H_o}{2\pi f_o Q C_2} = 19.9k \approx 20k \tag{21}$$

$$R_1 = \frac{Q}{2\pi f_o H_o C_1} = 19.9k \approx 20k \tag{22}$$

giving an actual calculated f_o and H_o of

$$H_o = 1/3 \left(1 + \frac{R_4}{R_3}\right) = 25.3 \tag{23}$$

$$f_o = \frac{Q}{2\pi R_1 C_1 H_o} = \frac{H_o}{2\pi R_2 C_2 Q} = 994.7 \text{ Hz} \tag{24}$$

The measured values of Q, H_o, and f_o using 1% components were 26.9, 26.3 and 996 respectively. Figure 13 shows the Bode plots of the high-pass, band-pass, and low pass outputs.

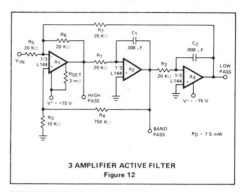

3 AMPLIFIER ACTIVE FILTER
Figure 12

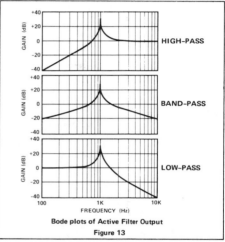

Bode plots of Active Filter Output
Figure 13

Micropower Double-Ended Limit Detector

The double-ended limit detector shown on Figure 14 uses three sections of an L144 and a CD4011 type CMOS NAND

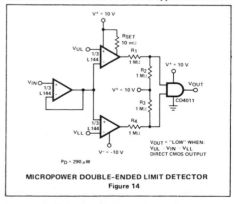

MICROPOWER DOUBLE-ENDED LIMIT DETECTOR
Figure 14

gate to make a very low power voltage monitor. If the input voltage V_{IN} is above V_{HIGH} or below V_{LOW} the output will be a logical high. If (and only if) the input is between the limits will the output be low. The 1 MΩ resistors R_1, R_2, R_3 and R_4 translate the bipolar ±10 V swing of the op amps to a 0 to 10 V swing acceptable to the ground-referenced CMOS logic.

Total power dissipation is typically 290 μW while in limit and 330 μW while out of limit. Within the ±9 V input range of the circuit the comparator resolution is typically 2 mV with the offset adjust determined by trimming V_{HIGH} and V_{LOW}. Since the L144 is operating at only 14.5 μA of supply current the slew rate is a corresponding low .063V/ μsec.

GLOSSARY

amplifier: a device which draws power from a source other than the input signal and develops an output signal that reproduces the essential features of the input signal at an increased level of voltage, current, or power.

analog: in electronic computers, a system in which the performance of measurements provides information concerning a class of mathematical operations.

analog computer: a computer that operates on the basis of a physical analogy of a mathematical operation.

bandwidth. see Unity-gain Bandwidth; Full-Power Response.

bias current: see Input Bias Current.

bode plot: a straight-line approximation to a frequency response curve which provides phase-response criteria.

breakpoint: a point on a Bode plot where a slope change occurs owing to a pole or zero at that frequency. A pole is a frequency that makes a mathematical function infinite; a zero is a frequency that makes the function zero.

chopper-stabilized amplifier: an amplifier stabilized against dc drift by breaking up the input signal to obtain an ac waveform that can be processed by an ac-coupled amplifier.

closed-loop gain: the gain of an op amp with a negative-feedback loop.

common-mode gain: the ratio of the output voltage of a differential amplifier to the common-mode input voltage. (The common-mode gain of an ideal differential amplifier is zero.)

common-mode input: an input voltage common to the two inputs of a differential amplifier.

common-mode voltage: the average of the two voltages applied to the inputs of a differential amplifier.

common-mode rejection ratio (CMRR): the ratio of the differential voltage gain of an amplifier to its common-mode voltage gain.

comparator: a differential-input amplifier utilized to compare the voltage levels at its two inputs, and having high gain so that only small voltage differences are required to switch the output voltage from one polarity to the other.

compensation: the shaping of an op-amp frequency response in order to achieve stable operation in a particular configuration.

differential amplifier: an amplifier that steps up the voltage difference between its two inputs.

differential input resistance: the effective resistance between the two inputs of an op amp when operated in the open-loop mode.

differential-mode gain: the ratio of the output voltage of a differential amplifier to the differential-mode input voltage.

differential-mode input: the voltage difference between the two inputs of a differential amplifier.

differential output amplifier: an amplifier that has two outputs of opposite gain polarity with respect to a given input.

differentiator: a passive differentiator employs a series RC circuit to develop an output that is roughly equal to the rate of change (roc) of the input waveform. An active differentiator also utilizes an op amp to obtain an output that is precisely equal to the roc of the input waveform.

drift: see Input Bias Current Drift; Input Offset Current Drift; Input Offset Voltage Drift.

FDNR: an abbreviation for frequency-dependent negative resistance; a type of active circuit employed in some low-pass filter configurations.

feedback: return of a portion of the output signal from a device to the input of the device.

feedback factor, β: that fraction of an output signal that is fed back to the input.

frequency compensation: see Compensation.

full-power factor, f_p: the maximum frequency at which an op amp can supply its rated output voltage and current without significant distortion.

function generator: an active configuration that produces an output signal related to an input signal (or locally generated signal) by a specified function or functions.

frequency response: see Unity-gain Bandwidth; Full-power Response.

gain: see Open-loop Gain; Loop Gain.

gain-bandwidth product: the product of the closed-loop gain and the closed-loop bandwidth. Often a constant in op-amp configurations.

gain error: the difference between the measured closed-loop gain of an op amp and the ideal gain predicted by theory.

gyrator: an op-amp circuit that simulates inductance; used in some active filters.

hysteresis: a lag in transfer response of comparators that are controlled by positive feedback, which results in different trip points for the two directions of output transition.

input bias current: the current that must be supplied to each input of an op amp to ensure proper biasing of the differential input stage. These are the bias currents that provide zero output voltage when the signal and input offset voltages are zero.

input bias current drift: the rate of change of input bias current with temperature or with time.

input capacitance: see Common-Mode Input Capacitance: Differential Input Capacitance.

input offset current: the difference between the input bias currents flowing into each input of an op amp, when the op amp output is at zero potential.

input offset current drift: the rate of change of input offset current with temperature or with time.

input offset voltage: the voltage that must be applied across the two inputs of an op amp in order to produce zero potential at the output.

input offset voltage drift: the rate of change of input offset voltage with temperature or with time.

input protection: protective means applied to the input of a device for prevention of damage owing to application of excessive input voltage.

input resistance: see Common-mode Input Resistance; Differential Input Resistance.

instrumentation amplifier: a dc-coupled differential-input amplifier with internal feedback for development of a specified voltage gain.

integrator: a passive integrator employs a series RC circuit to develop an output that is roughly equal to the integral (summation) of the initial input current with respect to time. An active integrator also utilizes an op amp to obtain an output that is precisely equal to the integral of the initial input current with respect to time.

inverting amplifier: an op amp with a feedback configuration which produces an output that is 180° out of phase with the input signal (produces an output polarity reversal).

isolation amplifier: an amplifier with high-impedance high-voltage isolation between input and output common components.

latch-up: a characteristic of certain kinds of op amps to remain in positive or negative saturation when subjected to a differential input voltage higher than rated.

logarithmic amplifier: an amplifier that develops an output voltage which is proportional to the logarithm of the input signal.

loop gain, Aβ: also called closed-loop gain; the gain around a feedback loop formed by an amplifier and its feedback network.

noninverting amplifier: an op amp with feedback which produces an output that is in phase with the input signal.

offset current: see Input Offset Current.

offset voltage: see Input Offset Voltage.

open-loop gain: the ratio of the output signal voltage of an op amp to the associated input signal voltage with the feedback loop open-circuited.

operational amplifier, op amp: a high-gain dc-coupled amplifier with differential input (or with both differential input and differential output), having high input impedance and low output impedance; also called an operational voltage amplifier.

operational transconductance amplifier: an op amp similar to the operational voltage amplifier, except that it has very high output impedance.

output offset voltage: the output voltage of a negative-feedback op-amp circuit when the input voltage is zero. An ideal op amp has zero offset voltage.

output protection: protective means for the output of a device, as output-current limiting provided for an operational amplifier.

sample-hold circuit: a device arranged to produce an output that follows an input signal, and then holds the instantaneous value of the signal when the hold signal is applied.

signal processor: a device arranged to convert or operate on input signals by analyzing, routing, rectifying, sampling, averaging, etc.

single-ended: denoting a single input or output, instead of a pair as in differential input or output.

slew rate: the maximum rate of change of the output voltage of an op amp as it swings from positive to negative saturation, or vice versa, in response to a square-wave push-pull (differential-mode) input.

summing junction: a junction of feedback and input resistors of a feedback network at which the signal currents from input resistors are summed.

unity-gain bandwidth, f_c**:** the frequency at which the open-loop gain of an op amp crosses zero dB (unity voltage gain).

varactor amplifier: a modulated-carrier dc-coupled amplifier that employs capacitance modulation of varactor diodes in response to low-frequency signals so that the signal can be processed by ac-coupled amplifiers.

virtual ground: a characteristic of the summing junction of an inverting op amp, which junction rests virtually at ground potential owing to the very high open-loop gain of the op amp.

voltage follower: an op amp with a direct feedback connection from output to inverting input which results in an output signal that follows the voltage at the noninverting input of the op amp.

INDEX